Number Nineteen ~ 2010

WRITINGS
New Millennium

Winner of a Golden Press Card Award for Excellence

Edited by Don Williams
who dedicates this issue

To
Steve and Liz Petty

for grace and good cheer
through all kinds of weather

Don Williams, *Editor*
Contributing Editors: *Laura Still, Doris Ivie, Sarah Mate, Marilyn Kallet,*
Cathy Kodra, Ouida Williams, Everette Bach, Marianne Chrystalbridge,
Renee Epling, David Hunter, Jon Manchip White and Allen Wier

Associate Editor: *Steve Petty*
General Submissions Editor: *Elizabeth Petty**
Assistant Editors: *Jeanne Tredup, Alexis Williams, Lawrence Duby*
Will Rickenbach, Nancy Rickenbach, Travis Williams, Justin Williams

Cover Art, 'World Enough and Time,' by David Joyner
Cover Design by *Rhonda Day of Hart Graphics*
Inside Typesetting & Layout by *Don Williams*
Special Thanks to Nikki Giovanni for judging our Summer 2009 competition
(award recipients to appear in our 2010-11 anthology).
Thanks also to *Don and Bev Tredup and family* of Kenosha, WI
and *John and Margie Richardson,* who were present at the birth.

Website by *Mark Plemmons,* **www.NewMillenniumWritings.com,**
Facebook site by *Steve Petty* and *R. J. McCoy.*
Search for *New Millennium Writings* on Facebook and become our fan.

Teachers and workshop leaders may purchase *NMW* at group discount rates.
email StevePetty@live.com, DonWilliams7@charter.net,
or visit www.newmillenniumwritings.com

ISSN 1086-7678, ISBN 1-888338-26-1 CPDA BIPAD No. 89927

New Millennium Writings is published annually. Additional copies may be purchased as stated above or send $12 per copy to **NMW, PO Box 2463, Knoxville, TN, 37901.** For rules of the twice-annual *NMW* Writing **Awards** for Fiction, Poetry and Nonfiction, visit **www.writingawards.com** or address envelopes to "Awards." Include SASE.

* **Contributors** Guidelines: We accept general submissions only in the months of January through April. We pay two free copies for poetry, upon acceptance. For fiction and nonfiction we pay $100 plus two copies, except for top prize-winners, who receive $1,000. See **Awards Guidelines, Page 22**. We do not accept general submissions online or by email. So when submitting for publication *outside* the contests, address envelopes to **Submissions Editor, 612 Gist Creek Rd., Sevierville, TN, 37876.** Include email address and/or letter-size SASE for response only. We're especially interested in **interviews, profiles and tributes to famous writers, living or dead. Allow six weeks for reply.** Include letter-size SASE or email address for response only. We return manuscripts only in hardship cases.

Contents ~ Featured Writers

The Late John Updike, on God, Rabbits, Sex & Writing, *88*

Of all the celebrity deaths of 2009, the toughest for *NMW* was that of John Updike, who died of lung cancer on Jan. 27, 2009. The self-effacing man of tact, taste and sometime flamboyant letters brought instant credibility to *New Millennium Writings* in 1996 when he agreed to be interviewed for our upstart literary journal. Here's that first-ever *NMW* author profile, anachronisms and all.

Photo by Jill Krementz   *~ Read Our Janus File tribute by Don Williams*

~ *Quick Tour* ~

On Obama, Updike, Other Scribes And Teachers of Scribes

Consider how the striking of clocks at midnight, Dec. 31, 1999, rendered our name obsolete.

At least, certain critics and friends said so. I never saw it that way. For the rest of our lives we'll live in the new millennium unless the world's amazing intelligentsia, aided by endlessly flashing ones and zeroes, comes up with some Forever Formula to drastically extend our lives, surely a mixed blessing. Either way, this thousand-year cycle we entered a decade ago has barely begun, Andrew Marvell's "winged chariot" notwithstanding.

True, it hasn't felt much like a new millennium. Perhaps childishly some of us looked to the new era as a time when humans would emerge from our planetary nursery and set aside childish things such as war, economic hooliganism and environmental abuse. Our species would graduate to embrace the shining chalice of our Whole Earth and drink deep her royal blue promise.

For us, the Supreme Court majority's choice for the new millennium's first president, in 2000, was a buzz-kill, followed by years of nightmare hangover. And so it was with great celebration that many of us embraced Barack Hussein Obama. If he could begin turning the tide on global warming, build down nukes, end America's wars, domestic spying, torture and shadowy government enties, he just might deliver us into a New Millennium worthy of the name.

That's turning out to be a big *if.* As this is written, the jury's out.

Still, I make no apologies for supporting the new guy in my commentary and in these pages. As prize-winning poet **Naomi Lowinsky** writes, "There is a place in poetry where the spiritual and the political meet...."

Most of the writing herein is apolitical. Still, some political writing pertains, and I've been criticized for mixing the twain. Poet **Peter Lopatin** agreed to accept his Honorable Mention in a recent *NMW* contest only after I offered to acknowledge his objection to our **Obama Millennial Award**, which we bestowed in the spring.

I made the offer for two reasons: First, I know what it's like to take a stand, and I can appreciate Lopatin's grit even while disagreeing. Second, I wanted his fine poem in our anthology. In an email to the poet, I defended our Obama awards so:

"Obama's a published poet, and quite a worthy one," I wrote. As evidence, check out **Obama's poem, "Pop,"** inside. And I continued, "Much as I despised Bush, I wrote a column praising him as a fellow distance-runner and a worthy one, so there is a certain consistency here."

Furthermore, "Obama achieved great distinctiveness—if not distinctive greatness—by becoming the first person of color to serve as president.

This is no mean achievement and is deserving of commendation from those who celebrate diversity. It was a big deal that he got elected.

"I have no pictures of Obama on my walls. Still, I thought his election was seminal, worth noting in the same way *NMW* recognized the dawning of a new millennium with a special Y2K Award in 2000. That's why we did it. For that I don't apologize."

If *NMW* and I are around when humans return to the moon or when the first woman's elected president, you can bet we'll acknowledge such seminal events, politics be damned. Otherwise, we will have diminished our claim to the name, *New Millennium Writings*... at least as we see it.

NMW has always been a place where famous voices from the past serve as heralds and mentors to emerging scribes. To that end, our first issue, Spring 1996, contained a feature we still continue, called the **Janus File,** after the Roman god. Janus is usually depicted with two faces looking in opposite directions. That's because Saturn graced him with the gift to see both future and past. Janus was the patron of new beginnings, herald and seer of new ages, economic enterprises, historical ages and seminal influences, according to an entry in **Wikipedia**.

OK, Wikipedia is subject to criticism, but given it's description of *NMW* as "a major literary magazine" how can I object? That was our goal. We evolved into the annual anthology you hold in your hands and an online presence at **NewMillenniumWritings.com** but I digress....

"Janus was also the God of gates, bridges... the progression of past to future, of one condition to another, of one vision to another, the growing up of young people, and of one universe to another," states the Wikipedia entry.

In this issue our resident Janus pays tribute to the late **John Updike**, who died in January, 2009, but who was vibrantly alive when we profiled him in that first issue. He brought instant credibility, and he taught me a lot about writing and life.

Which brings me to teachers. *New Millennium Writings* is reaching out to college, university and other writing programs. **On page 196, you'll find our first-ever *NMW Study Guide*,** which suggests provocative strategies for discussing these works in classrooms and workshops, as well as independently by emerging writers of any age or level of achievement. Here you'll find ways to assess character, tone, theme, opening lines, wordplay, and myriad other aspects of writing. Add to that **writing advice from prize-winners** and **"Break These Rules..."** starting on the last page of this book, and you have a bona fide instrument for discerning the themes and techniques employed by practicing scribes here at the nexus of fiction, creative nonfiction and poetry—one of many crossroads literary, political and philosophical where we at *NMW* take our stand.

Namaste, Shalom, Salaam, Shantih and Peace,

Don Williams

New Millennium Writings

Is pleased to present the New Millennium

Short-short Fiction Awards

Winning entries appear on pages 8-21 (see Contents pages)

Winter 2008-09

Allison Alsup, New Orleans, LA, *Grass Shrimp, 8*

Summer 2008

Tim Johnson, West Linn, OR, *America the Beautiful, 12*
Barbara Zimmermann, Yorktown, IN, *Southern Discomfort, 18*

HONORABLE MENTIONS

Summer 2008	Winter 2008-09
Katherine Bach, Seymour, TN	Phyllis Aboaf, San Francisco, CA
Jim Bainbridge, Los Angeles, CA	Hal Ackerman, Los Angeles, CA
Gertrude Bishop, Gainesville, FL	Kate B. Adams, Charleston, SC
Robert Davis, Newark, DE	David Anderson, Gardnerville, NV
Frank Edwards, Hattiesburg, MS	Marian Armstrong, Piermont, NY
Erin Ergenbright, Portland, OR	James Bainbridge, Los Angeles, CA
Paula Friedman, Parkdale, OR	Maija Devine, Lee's Summit, MO
Rusty Harris, Simi Valley, CA	Sherryl Gardner, San Jose, CA
Helen Heath, San Anselmo, CA	Ronald W. Jaeger, Austin, TX
Excell N. Hunter, Pomona, CA	Jacob Jaffe, Bronx, NY
Reba Ann Karp, Virginia Beach, VA	Henry Lissauer, Voorhees, NJ
Steve Machuga, Middletown, CT	Alexandria Marzano, Cambridge, MA
Djelloul Marbrook, Germantown, NY	Steve Matchett, Charlotte, NC
Rickey Pittman, Monroe, LA	Rodney Nelsestuen, Woodbury, MN
E. K. Schuster, Austin, TX	Carol Parikh, Brookline, MA
Barbara Shapiro, Ithaca, NY	Earl Privette, Rapidan, VA
Louise Farmer Smith, DC	Michaela Roessner, Tehachapi, CA
D.C. Thomas, Pittsburgh, PA	Elizabeth Simms, St. Charles, MO
Chelsea Trent, Warrensburg, MO	Kurt Steinwand, Brandon, FL
Bonnie West, St. Paul, MN	Joan Swift, Edmonds, WA

Allison Alsup
Grass Shrimp

*B**at has said something that most in our fishing camp cannot believe. A male shrimp can become a female. He cuts them open, not to eat or sell, but to examine. The males die sooner he explains. Becoming a female is a matter of survival. Xin says he doesn't believe this; it goes against all nature. He also says such experiments are wasteful. Why study what can be sold? But that is why we call Bat as we do; his mind hangs upside down.*

I, for one, believe Bat. What was once one thing can become another. It is an idea everyone here should understand. In China, we were fathers, sons and now, we are quite another: bachelors and orphans, all of us. I was once a tailor with a plate glass window and bolts of embroidered silk; now I mend nets and sails and peel speckled shells from the grass shrimp that wander the muddy bottoms of this ghostland bay. Here, we become what is necessary to live.

Our fishing camp, one of dozens along this coast, sits on a bend in the shore like the shallow curve of an oyster. Two small hills rise to either side and it is halfway up one of these slopes, tucked between sweet yellow grass and bitter green blades of Eucalyptus, that Xin and I share a cabin. Xin left this morning for San Francisco, crossing the bay in the new shirt I sewed for him. Like most, he will send money home to his wife and if there is extra, sleep with his whore. I no longer

'I am awed by the emotional and physical resilience of the early generations of Chinese immigrants to California. They did most of the toughest work in the face of blatant racism. I am also interested in what I see as their between-ness. Gold Mountain men were dubbed Jinshanke, a term which meant they were no longer strictly Chinese; of course, whites did not perceive them as Americans either. "Grass Shrimp" is an attempt to extend this between-ness to gender and to explore the sorts of intimacies that must have existed in a "bachelor society" in which men outnumbered women as much as twenty to one. The self-hermaphroditing shrimp is indeed a theory posed by some biologists. I have since taken this piece and am at work on a novel. I hope to turn these two pages into two hundred.'

~ Allison Alsup

ask about such things. Like most, he still dreams of returning home to Canton, to Pearl River. I do not. I wrote my wife, *Tell them I have died. You are free.*

Bat and I sit on his porch sipping black tea. It is a late February afternoon like any other, clear and very cool; a brush-like wind paints everything with salt. Ahead, six men rub tung oil on the redwood hull of a beached sampan. In this camp, there are only two seasons: shrimping and waiting to shrimp. Xin says my fingers are too fine for planting nets and that my bones are as thin as an egret's. I like it when he says this. In a few weeks, the season will begin again. But there is always work; even now my mending basket waits. I ignore it and as always, look for Xin's boat to return.

Here is what I see: the water's edge runs like a thick white seam connecting a blue silk swath to burlap sands. A dock juts out, its weathered piers like rough stitches. Button boats rise and fall beyond the break. The world is a perfect robe, I tell Bat even though I know this camp, this life is far from perfection. Just a dozen miles away, San Francisco breaks its back to rebuild from quake and fire; so many still in tents. But the city is not visible from our little bend and however hard San Francisco must work, it is no more than us. At this moment, I feel that all we need is here.

"The emperor's robe is the world," Bat gently corrects. We list the elements that must appear on the Son of Heaven's brilliant yellow robes: the nine dragons with feet of five claws, the four mountains, the twelve symbols of luck, each a small prayer on the tongue. I do not know how Bat knows such things but I have learned not to ask about the life before this one.

"The emperor will fall," Bat says suddenly. He does not mean that the emperor will die; the Son of Heaven is still a child. Bat squints as if the coming change were visible over the breakwater. "More tea?" he asks.

*

For over a year, Xin and I have shared two rooms; one with a stove and table and the other for sleeping. Over the months, I have pushed our bed mats together, movements as small as stitches. Once Xin noticed and pushed the beds apart, but the next day, I began to move them back and he has not pushed them away since. Tonight, they almost touch.

When Xin returns, I have already lighted the lantern. His long braid is gone.

"You look like a ghost," I tell him and hold up the flame to see his new American haircut. I cannot imagine him returning to Pearl River now.

"It is easier this way," he explains. It could mean any number of things. Then he looks at the bedrolls. "You have cleaned," he says, nothing more.

Xin lights a second lantern and reads to me from a paper bought in the city. The ghost mayor wants to rebuild the crumbled Chinatown at the city's fringes. I light the stove against the falling fog and we eat a simple soup of bass and scallions. Xin lights one cigarette after another. Twice, he opens the front door to stare at nothing. The voices of drunken men outside Quan's grocery carry up the hill. Xin is restless; he has not been to see his whore.

Later, when the room is dark, I picture the emperor's ceremonial robes. To wear the universe! To face a certain direction, to recite a certain prayer, to make a certain offering. There was a time when I took comfort in the thought of an ordered world, times when even here, I felt the reach of the emperor's pale, perfect hands. But the world is not still; eventually, everything shifts like the tides and now I find myself thinking of what Bat has said, of grass shrimp, of the speckled brown bodies that wander these muddy flats. One thing can become another. I touch Xin's cropped hair where his braid used to fall. *Husband*, I whisper. Xin turns towards me and I open my robe to show him what I too, have become.

First Place Short-Short Fiction Prize
~ In the 26th Consecutive NMW Awards (tie) ~

Tim Johnson
America The Beautiful

L isten to this. It's been six months since I stopped drinking. Made it through the whole summer, which is the hardest time of the year for people like me. Except for maybe winter.

School's in full swing now. My son is a freshman this year and he got a part in the fall musical, which is usually only for upperclassmen. My daughter is a senior and she got to sing the "National Anthem" at the home football game last Friday night. She was practicing all week, in her room, in the shower, in her car. God I hate that song.

*

When you stop giving in to an addiction the biggest change is how much you re-engage with real people again. When you stop hiding out, alone with your self-loathing, careful not to get caught, you get back to having a personality again. You're not afraid. You take chances.

Things start to happen....

There's a soup kitchen near where I work and if I take a walk at lunch I pass by it on my way to Powell's Bookstore. At lunchtime there's always a big line of homeless people, mostly men, waiting for the proverbial free lunch. Maybe thirty people, sitting, standing, smoking, looking hopeless or impatient or scary, sometimes all at once.

As I walk past the end of the line I see a group of three ex-con-

'I don't have much advice having not been an active writer for many years. But in picking it up again I can offer a few observations: Writing only works if you're ruthlessly honest. Whether it's autobiography, nonfiction, or complete fantasy my writing suffers the minute I try to make it something it's not. Words matter. If you take care putting them together you can make a real impact on somebody reading them. People want to be moved. They not only like it, they expect it. It's why they read or watch TV or go to the movies. So try to move them.'

~ Tim Johnson

looking guys with tattoos. One guy catches my eye, takes a smoke and growls, "How 'bout you gimme some change buddy?" and blows smoke at me.

I keep walking and say, "I don't think so."

He says, "Thanks shithead." His buddies laugh.

Normally I'd just keep walking. The old normal, I mean. Before I cleaned up. I grew up in a fairly rough part of Detroit so in my youth I was a lot more mouthy in these situations. I guess I've mellowed since then but I still knew the drill. You can take the boy out of Detroit...

I stop and turn back.

"What did you say?"

His friends stop laughing but this guy just looks me over real slow and says, "Nothin'."

"Because I thought you just told me to give you money and then called me a shithead."

His friend takes a step towards me and says, "Hey fuck you, asshole."

The guy doesn't flinch and says, "You look like you doin' alright, man, and we got nothin'. I'm just askin' for spare change, you know? No big deal, so you can just go back to your little cubicle or whatever."

I should leave but the 'cubicle' reference pisses me off. It is sort of little.

I say, "I work all day for my money, dude. Why should I give you some?"

The two friends go, "Duuuude."

The guy says, "Hey, we work. We workin' the streets, you know?" His buddies laugh. "We workin' you, dude. Why don't you just give me five bucks. You can spare five bucks, right? Man like you?"

"Yeah, I got five bucks." I pull a five out of my pocket. "But what would you do for it?"

His friend gets closer and says, "Hey man, he don't do that kind of faggot shit. You sayin' my friend here's a faggot?"

"I'm not talkin' about faggot shit. I'm talking about working." I hold up the five. "You do something for me, I *pay* you five bucks. I don't *give* you five bucks. That's how it works."

Now pretty much the whole line is looking my way, wondering where this is going. I'm kind of wondering that myself.

This guy knows he's got an audience too. He backs off.

"Hey I'd love to man, but I gotta catch lunch, you know? Around here, they don't wait."

His friends laugh and knock fists. The front door to the kitchen opens up and people turn to face front again. Lunch is served.

I think about it for a second. I hold up my five again.

"I'll pay you five bucks to sing the Star-Spangled Banner."

The back half of the line turns to look again.

The guy says, "Fuck you, man."

A short fat woman with a limp breaks line. "I'll sing it."

He holds out his arm to block her and says, "Back off, Theresa." And then to me, "You'll give me five bucks to sing the Star-Spangled Banner."

"Hey, it's not an easy song. It's worth five bucks. You know all the words?"

Theresa says, "I know the words."

The guy says, "Yeah, I know all the fuckin' words. It's just a stupid fuckin' idea. You tryin' to make me look stupid, man?"

"Hey, it's a great song," I lie. "It's the National Anthem. And not everybody can sing it. If you can do it, I'll pay you five bucks."

The door is open but most of the people in line aren't going in. They're watching the guy. A man and a woman waiting to cross at the light have a green light, but they're not moving either. Another guy who passed by stops at a safe distance and turns back to watch.

The guy takes a slow drag on his cigarette and then turns to his buddies. "You believe this motherfucker?"

The one friend says, "Do it Jimmy. It's five bucks." The other one says "Yeah, man, do it."

Just then a cop car pulls around the corner and stops at the sight of this face-off at the soup kitchen, the long line not moving. Two cops get out. Some in the line move toward the door, but most stay.

The first cop, a big blond-haired kid, asks what's going on.

I explain the pending transaction.

The other cop, shorter and heavy, laughs out loud. He seems to know the guy.

"Well, go ahead, Jimmy," he says, laughing. Jimmy looks around, up at the cops, back at me.

Suddenly these aren't just scenery people any more. They're not just pictures in my head.

"Ten bucks," he says to me. The crowd gasps. The blond cop snorts. This guy's got balls.

I reach in my wallet and pull out another five.

"Five just to sing it. Five more if you get all the words right."

Nobody's moving. Two of the kitchen helpers appear at the kitchen door, watching.

Jimmy hands his cigarette to his friend to hold. Then he starts, real quiet.

"O-oh say..." and breaks off right away, shaking his head, clearing his throat. Somebody titters.

He starts again.

"O-oh say can you see...."

He cracks on "see" and stops, then slowly starts again, lower this time. Smart guy. He doesn't sound bad in this key.

He gets to "last gleaming" and hesitates. He's slow through this part but remembers it's "*broad* stripes and *bright* stars."

He even gets "perilous fight" correct. Most people sing "perilous night."

He sings "on the ramparts" instead of "o'er," but I let it go.

He gets to "were so...."

Then he stops.

"... were so...."

Somebody in the crowd groans. Somebody else whispers, "I told you, man."

15

He looks at his buddies, like he's going to hit one of them or cry or both. One mumbles the line before, hoping to get a running start and remember the words. The other one joins in.

"...on the ramberts we watched, were so... were so... *shit!*"

I'm starting to feel bad about this.

Then I hear, "..were so gallantly streaming."

It's the short heavy cop, singing loud and in a surprisingly good baritone voice.

Jimmy smiles and nods his head and sings it again... "on the ramparts we watched, were so gallantly streaming!"

The "rockets' red glare" goes very well after that and I get the feeling Jimmy's home free now. He knows it too. I guess I'm out ten bucks.

But then something else happens.

When he gets to "...flag was still there," he slows down. Like he's heading for the big finish or something, like at a game. He's really getting into it, right there on the street, right out in front of everybody.

When he opens his mouth for that last "Oh say..." I hear three other voices with him. The heavy cop is one of them. And one of his buddies. And Theresa.

On "banner yet wave" there are eight voices.

And then literally everybody else on that corner, the cops, the homeless people, and everybody looking on, including me, is singing out at the top of their voices, "O'er the land of the free." We all hold it out a long time. I even hear a few people reach for the high note.

"AND THE HOME... OF THE... BRAVE."

And then everybody breaks into applause and shouts and whistles. Just like a Friday night, except without the beer.

Jimmy's friends clap him on the back. The cops clap him on the back. He looks up to see the kitchen help smiling and clapping, and at the business people in their dark suits and hard shoes applauding.

He looks up at me.

I give him the two fives. Then I take out my last ten from my wallet and give him that too.

"Good job," I tell him.

He takes it and nods once, shoves it in his pocket. They all start moving into the kitchen for lunch. The business people cross the street. The cops get back in their patrol car and drive off.

I turn to walk to the bookstore, not knowing exactly what just happened, but knowing it wouldn't have happened six months ago.

"Hey!"

I look back and there's Theresa at the door.

"What I get for America the Beautiful?"

Barbara Zimmermann
Southern Discomfort

ouise sat at the far table in McDonald's, her shoulders hunched as she concentrated on the form before her. Social Security Number, Work Experience, Education. They would be quite fortunate to hire someone like me, she thought, her thin fingers tightly gripping the pen in her right hand.

She filled in the information, underlining her experience as a teacher and her degree, cautiously giving references that she knew would vouch for her sterling character. She glanced about the restaurant: a foursome of teenage girls sat at one table, eating French fries, their table manners *despicable*. Perhaps she could persuade the manager to put sprigs of fresh flowers—daisies or a pink carnation with a stem of baby's breath—in a glass vase on each table. Add a touch of class.

"Well, are you finished, Ma'am?"

Startled, Louise glanced up at the manager who was scanning the paper on the table. "Why, yes, sir, all done." She smiled at the young man, surely no older than twenty-one if a day.

He sat down across from her and held out his hand. She placed her hand in his, pressing her palm into his warm flesh, and said, "Louise Couvrette. And you're?"

'"Southern Discomfort" is the result of a writing exercise that required me to choose a name from a list of famous characters in literature and to select from another list a contemporary setting and then come up with a conflict. Louise, an aging Southern belle in a predicament, learns panache will only take you so far, and yet retains her charm.'

~ Barbara Zimmermann

"Sal Romero," he said, slipping his hand from her grasp. "May I see your application?"

Oh, dear, she thought, he must think I'm quite forward. She lifted the linen handkerchief from her lap and twisted it in her hands, wishing she'd applied a fresh coat of lipstick. The light from the window, she was sure, magnified the lines grooved into her forehead, the puffiness beneath her eyes, the loosening flesh at the bend of her throat. Her mouth, she had always believed, was her most attractive feature: the thin upper lip with pointy tips and the full lower lip. That and her hands fluttering in concert with her spoken words and laughter bubbling forth at the appropriate moments, bedazzled her audience, she suspected.

As he read her resume, she thought of her barely adequate room at the YWCA with the beat-up dresser drawers, a lumpy bed, the common bathroom. The other residents complained about her long hot baths and the steamed-up mirror. Despite the discomforts, if she could make enough money to pay one more month's rent, her prospects, she was sure, would improve.

"Why aren't you teaching?"

She had prepared herself for that question, aware that she was overqualified to flip hamburgers. "I'm working on my memoir and I really want to have time to write. Teaching follows you home, grading and lesson plans. You know."

His translucent blue eyes fixed on hers as if he were consuming her words and regurgitating them right back at her. She hoped that he wouldn't probe further. She'd omitted the last high school at which she'd taught, certain that the brief indiscretion with the principal would remain her secret. She'd chosen her outfit carefully for the interview: a red jersey sheath with navy piping, and navy blue pumps. She'd curled her hair the night before, sleeping fitfully all night, bobby pins piercing her scalp and cutting into her fingers when she turned to lie in the fetal position, her hands clasped together beneath her cheek.

"At first you'd have to work the early shift, breakfast, seven to ten, five days a week."

"Why I didn't realize you opened so early. Isn't there a late shift available? I do believe a lady looks her best after a good night's rest, don't you?" She hoped that he was a gentleman who appreciated the time it took for a woman to cream her skin, apply makeup, spray Tabu at the pulse points and cleavage.

His arms were muscular, the short sleeves of his shirt straining against his biceps, and he had a wrestler's neck. She wondered if he drank beer straight from the bottle, belching uncouthly after guzzling the contents in one or two gulps. He'd need her tutelage on fine drinking: a martini or whiskey neat before dinner, sipping slowly to appreciate the warmth sliding down the throat and filling the chest with comfort. Why, she could invite him over one evening, after she'd worked there a week or so, fix him chicken-fried steak, creamed corn, sliced tomatoes. Later, she could play Dinah Washington's "Sunday Kind of Love," slow-step her way into his life.

"Sorry, best I could do is maybe an occasional night shift, seven to eleven, on Friday and Saturday. Otherwise, mornings. You've got to take what nobody else wants as the new kid."

He was smiling at her. She wet her lips and smiled back. Then it struck her that he could be betting on her turning down the gruesome hours.

"Yes, sir. I'll work it out." She couldn't imagine getting up at five in the morning to get ready. She wondered if she could just stay up all night, spray a touch of Tabu, gargle Listerine, then make it through three hours without accidentally dipping her hand into the boiling oil instead of the French fries or gagging when slapping raw hamburger onto the grill. She calculated the crumpled bills in her purse, forty-seven dollars or so. A week away from the poor farm.

He was frowning now, and he coughed before saying, "Okay, be here at six-forty-five in the morning."

She stood and held out her hand. He nodded. Blushing, she swept her right hand upwards to pat her hair and said, "You won't be sorry, Mr. Romero."

She could feel his eyes following her out the door and felt a pressure near her heart, a familiar warning sign that made her cringe. She straightened her shoulders, smoothed the front of her dress, her right hand lingering for a moment at her bosom before she turned to force a smile in his direction. She could only make out her own reflection in the window: the sun was low in the horizon, her top curls framed like a lop-sided tiara, and the passing traffic behind her, glittering streamers of chrome.

New Millennium Writings

Is pleased to present the New Millennium

Fiction Awards

Winning entries appear on pages 24-57

Winter 2008-09

Steve Fayer, Boston, MA, *Calliope, 24*

Summer 2008

Rusty Dolleman, San Francisco, CA, *Sheepdog, 43*

HONORABLE MENTIONS

Summer 2008

Becky Ann Bartlett, Nazareth, PA
Paul Byall, Bedminster, NJ
Jennifer Caloyeras, Los Angeles, CA
Linda Davis, Santa Monica, CA
Benjamin Doty, Mountain View, CA
Katharine Duckett, Powell, TN
Rose Hamilton-Gottlieb, Fullerton, CA
Jean Harper, Richmond, IN
Ronald N. Howland, Reading, MA
Liane LeMaster, Dunwoody, GA
Rachel May, Lincoln, NE
Deirdra McAfee, Richmond, VA
Devin Myers, Tucson, AZ
Natalie Pepa, Elgin, IL
Nicole Reid, Evansville, IN
Morgan Smith, Santa Fe, NM
Jessica Sneeringer, Bentonville, AR
Marci Stillerman, Rancho Mirage, CA
James Vescovi, New York, NY
Juliet Wittman, Boulder, CO

Winter 2008-09

Jacob Appel, Scarsdale, NY
Mark Bowers, Marshfield, MO
Luba Burtyk, Manhattan, NY
Kerri Campbell, Denver, CO
Megan Carter, Missoula, MT
Joan Corwin, Evanston, IL
Margarite Landry, Southborough, MA
Gregory Loselle, Southgate, MI
Jackie Davis-Martin, San Francisco, CA
Mark Mustian, Tallahassee, FL
Lucie Ogilvie, Kinsale, VA
Paula Paige, Cromwell, CT
Evan Rehill, San Francisco, CA
Adam Russ, Davis, CA
Lynn Sadler, Sanford, NC
Jennifer Sears, Brooklyn, NY
Eliezer Sobel, Richmond, VA
L.B. Thompson, Greenport, NY
Rachel Weaver, Louisville, CO
Mary Ziegler, Butte, MT

Steve Fayer
Calliope

*B*ut tell me a happy story," his great-granddaughter said.

"Don't know no happy ones," Ditch Pollard said.

The child, like most six-year-olds, took comfort in heroic myths progressing in a linear fashion that never did exist in the real world. He had tried to prepare her with stories that did not end well, stories that were his own childhood in disguise. But the girl had refused to absorb the sadness. She had known losses. What she wanted was fairy tales.

*

"Once upon a time," he began, "there was a princess who lived in Slaters Ridge. In the Catskill Mountains. In the state of New York."

"What color was she?" Callie said.

"Color don't matter."

"Does, too."

"Okay, she was the color of coffee in which some fool had poured too much cream."

"Coffee-colored?"

"Well, maybe more like honey. A honey-colored child."

"Like me?"

"Prettier than you, girl."

"Nobody's prettier than me."

*

"Her name was Calliope," he said. "From the Greek language. A slave name. The old masters showing off their classic education, you might say, and making a joke by naming those whom they considered

24

'My grandparents, Russian immigrants, owned a farm in the Catskills, on the fringes of the borscht circuit. It was on the farm that I first encountered the sensual young girl who was the model for the character, Rhoda. And it was in the village nearby that an old black man revealed to one of my cousins a cache of nude photographs taken years earlier. What happened to those once naked village girls? And to their young men? Decades later, fiction began to provide answers—in moments when I stopped directing the characters and simply listened to their lives. "Calliope," written as a separate story, eventually became the third installment of a four-part 45,000 word novella. In this episode, the child Calliope tries to reconcile words with perceived reality while the adults, most of them, have given up the effort. She was inspired by a friend whom I have always called "honey-colored child"—ever since a reporter described her that way during her arrest at a 1960s civil rights sit-in. She is one of those people who will not shut up when there is something that must be said, whose stubbornness can be a thorn in the side of friend and foe alike—particularly when justice is denied. It is my hope that the story communicates in some small way the little girl's potential for such lifelong honesty and courage. And joy. '

~ Steve Fayer

lesser humans with the names of muses and other gods and goddesses."

"You are already making this a sad story," the child said.

"Am not," he said. And grew silent.

"This princess," Callie said. "Her name sounds like mine. And my name is not joke-y."

"That's the thing," he said. "You take someone's joke, and you turn it into your own music. You tap your feet to it. You dance on it. And you come up with a beautiful riff, you come up with a name like Callie."

*

"So once upon a time there was a beautiful princess," he said. "With a name handed down from Olympus."

"Olympus?"

"A heaven," he said. "Somewheres down in the south of Europe."

It was an old and by now rehearsed pattern of call-and-response. The old man soon to celebrate his ninetieth birthday. The child fearful of losing him.

"Or maybe it was a mountain," he said.

"Like these mountains?"

"Well, these mountains are Dutch mountains. Before, I was talking about Greek mountains."

*

The girl slept in his arms. He had held children, and then grand-children against his chest. But this first great-grandchild, unlike the others, seemed hell-bent on erasing the years that stood between them. She flirted with him, breathed into his neck in her sleep, snored lightly there, compared her own fair skin against the wrinkled chestnut hue he owned, traced the cords of muscle that stood out on his bone-thin arms, rubbed her face on the calluses of his hands. With her father long gone, she was using him, Ditch thought, in the long and tangled process of learning womanhood. He hoped the child's beauty would be employed someday only to break men's hearts, that it would not be a curse to her—burdening her with the overblown expectations of others, making out of her a grown woman drowning in admiration, and bruised by the ugliness to which she would be inevitably attracted.

Ditch Pollard hoped that she would know in the moments when she was unloved and in disrepair that she had been loved, and had trusted a man in her life who had not betrayed her. That would be the sweetest way to immortality. Or so he told himself.

*

Once upon a time there had been a beautiful princess, he dreamed. In the town of Slaters Ridge. And her skin had been the color of chalk. Her hair as dark as a black woman's hair, and almost as tightly curled. The princess was white. But even before history was written down, her ancestors had lain with Africans. Sheba was one of her great great grandmothers. And this girl had given the eye to a boy with chestnut-dark skin, a nod to her history and his.

It was not the usual fairy tale. And he wished Callie would hurry and grow up so he could tell it to her before his own breath stopped.

The father of the princess hated people of color and would have shot-gunned the chestnut-skinned boy without a by-your-leave if he knew that boy had the eye of his elder daughter.

In the mid-1920s, he had been the only black child in the high school. Being only one, he was not deemed much of a threat. Taught Yiddish by the Jewish couple with whom he and his mother roomed, he was the town's good-natured joke. While his mother worked in the Sullivan County laundry, the boy labored at odd jobs—on a good day he could make a dollar and a half—helping to cut ice out of Stump Lake in the deep winter, digging ditches for the town when some of the old mains burst, mowing hotel lawns, sculpting hedges designed to keep out people like him.

There were no girls of color in the town. Only a few women of his mother's age come up from Georgia to the laundry. Except for the offices of his own right hand, he remained a virgin, clothed in an innocence of which his mother, an AME regular churchgoer, was particularly proud.

*

The chicken farm where he roomed with his mother was two miles up the road that led from the village to the ridge. The road led past the Pearl farm, the house a relic of the mid-1800s, paint peeling, main beams rotting with a tendency to sway just so you could notice in a late summer storm. Behind it stood a stout oaken barn, sheltering five or six milk cows. On the side of the barn was a chicken coop, with the standard assortment of birds for that time, White Leghorns, the big egg producers, and Barred Rocks for meat and brown eggs.

He passed the Pearl farm at least two times a day.

On rare occasions, he walked the hill after school with the Pearls' oldest daughter, Laurie. Sometimes accompanied by her younger sister, Alexandra, a girl of twelve or so, barely budding.

Ditch had a good mind for things mechanical. He thought that was why Laurie Pearl decided he could be trusted with her father's new Kodak camera. He soon learned it was not just the camera she would trust him with. She would put in his hands her own good name. And the good names of several others, male and female, in their small high school class. It would be in the barn of the Pearl farm—and in the abandoned settlement not far up the road—where their lives would take an unanticipated turn.

*

Callie shook him awake. "What about this child on the mountain?" she said. What about Calliope?"

"She swam every day," he said. "In the magic river called Neversink. And the child's long hair braided with cowrie shells streamed out behind her, the cowries protecting her, you know, and paying her way."

"Was it good hair?"

"Passably good."

"Good like mine?"

"Yes, good like yours. Fitting to her honey-color."

He paused while she let the scene play in her mind. "She don't have clothes on," Callie said.

Ditch had heard of old men who turned to sex talk with children. He did not want to be one of those old fools. "She does, too, have clothes on," he said. "A princess knows enough to cover her nakedness."

"So you can't see her titties," the child said.

"What's this about good hair and bad hair?" he said.

The child looked him over. Her great grandfather had skin dark as chestnut. His hair, what little he had left, tightly curled to his skull.

"I got good hair, my momma said. Other people, they got bad hair."

"White folks?"

"White folks have good hair," the child said. "Like me."

*

Laurie Pearl put her head against his chest. The cows in the dark barn stirred uneasily.

The girl's hair was like dark silk. He combed it with his fingers. The feel and scent of the hair was as erotic as the breasts which he dared not reach for.

"Different," Laurie Pearl said.

"Sure is."

"I want you to touch me all over," she whispered.

*

Ditch fled the barn. At age sixteen, he knew how the world worked. Ever since the end of the Great War, it seemed whites were beating on niggers all over the country. As if the energy stored up to fight the Hun had not been totally expended, and was turned now to fight the colored.

Even more powerful, however, was the fear of God's rules. His Christian faith was strong. And fornication no matter the color combination was an insult to the church and to its African Methodist Episcopal God. Not a god invented by Greeks. But the genuine article. At least that is what he had been taught.

The Yiddish-speaking Lithuanian couple, the Mintzes, with whom he and his mother boarded, believed in no God. They lived in sin in a community that seemed to shrug off the couple's defiance of social codes. Socialists, communists, were not that unusual among the Yiddish-speaking immigrants from eastern Europe. He had picked up their language, entering a universe of curses and creative insult, a world of undisguised physical function and bawdiness. In its rhythms, it seemed opposite to the language of his mother and her friends, their soft-spoken Southern-ness laced with plantation idiom from a world of servitude only half a century dead. But despite the Jews' privilege of their white skin, beneath the rivers of sound even as a child he had observed widely divided but parallel courses. If Jews insulted, colored folks signified. If blue-collar Jews self-deprecated in their name-calling, it was not a far leap to his mother sniffing at "house niggers." If Molly Mintz made fun of "the goyim," he also heard his mother's coded back-of-the-hand talk about "Mister Charley and Miss Anne." His mother, Truth Pollard, had come up from Georgia, the daughter of a couple themselves conceived in bondage. His father had disappeared in the environs of Stone Mountain, done in or done gone, his mother said. Either fate not unusual.

He thought he could broach the problem of Laurie Pearl with Molly Mintz, their landlady, freethinker and freelover that she was. More than once, Molly had told him she loved him like a son. But what if he was wrong about her? What if whiteness bred loyalties he did not yet understand? Would Molly turn him in for the crime of thinking miscegenation? Or, at the least, would Molly get Laurie in trouble by telling on her to Sam Pearl, a shotgun wielding fool in bloused trousers and high Russian boots, who had made clear his contempt for every colored man and woman who had come to work in the town.

The night Laurie offered herself, Ditch ran from the Pearl barn into the woods that grew high above the farm. He heard Laurie calling into the darkness, calling his name, a damn fool thing to do given that her father Sam Pearl was probably somewhere on the property. Ditch trembled. He did indeed want to touch all those secrets she had offered. There was a dark place in his soul. And Laurie Pearl had walked into that center, her wonderful breasts pushing against the whiteness of her middy blouse, her nipples erect and visible even through the opacity of her underwear.

Ditch Pollard was shaking with desire.

*

He had warned Callie. She had a habit of raiding his collection of stones and pebbles worn smooth by the action of the Neversink River nearby. The child always sucking on a stone as if it were a hard candy, rolling it from side to side in her mouth, inserting it into the gaps from which baby teeth had disappeared.

"I am going to die," the child screamed. Her eyes were bright with terror. She jumped into his lap, attempted to burrow beneath his outer self, perhaps imagining herself small enough to hide so deep in a wrinkle that the reaper would not find her.

"Nobody gonna kill you," he said.

"Killed myself."

He patted the wing bones in her back. "How's that?"

"I swallowed the stone," she said. "The stone I had in my mouth."

"Given your long-lived ancestors," he said. "You got approximately one hundred years before you croak."

"But it will grow into a rock inside of me," Callie said. "And then into a mountain. It will take me over."

*

He made a deal with the child. They would examine her stools for the next day or two. He assured her that she would pass the stone easy as pie."

"Like corn?"

"Yes, like corn."

On the second day, she called him into the bathroom. The crisis was over. But the idea that she took death so seriously stayed with him. The child was not too young to fear for her life. He feared for it as well. But it would not be a polished pebble cast up by a magic river that threatened her. It would be this village. The high ridge that loomed over it, making everyone feel small. The child's mother was already lost, nodding in some doorway in far-off Brooklyn. So it was her grandmother, his daughter, who looked almost as old as he and creaked when she walked, a woman with bones as brittle as bad concrete, who had taken charge of the child. So Callie had a right to fear. Those charged with the child's caretaking stood on the universe's edge, divers on the high board.

You cannot make a contract with life, he wanted to tell her. Or one with another human being that will hold up for eternity in God's court. It was all complicated. And sometimes it hurt his head to think about it. Words that he required were buried somewhere inside his skull, and refused to make themselves available.

*

The camera was an up-to-date 1926 model made upstate in Rochester, a brand-new Kodak Autographic. It unfolded from its flat leather case into what looked like a steam locomotive, the bellows pulling out to form the engine. It was one of the most beautiful devices he had ever seen, unblemished chrome and stainless steel, the lenses highly polished. Even the instruction booklet seemed a work of art. A few days later, Laurie Pearl again put it into his hands.

"Could you take my picture?" she asked.

Yes, he could learn to take her picture, he told her. Then I will get some film this week, she said, and then ran off into the gathering dark, her white middy blouse half-pulled from the waist of her skirt, her figure receding toward the Pearl house as she cradled the camera in her arms.

*

"Black people ain't black," Callie announced at table. "Black people is brown. Or coffee-colored. Or honey-colored. And any fool can see that black people has been mis-named.

The child could not be silenced.

"I ain't never seen a white person, either," she said. "They pinkish, or greyish, or brownish."

"Well, don't worry about it," her grandmother said. "The older you get, the less you will bother to see. It just gets easier."

"You're fooling with the child's mind," Ditch said. He turned to Callie. "If you're smart about it, you'll grow up to see more than any of us ever saw."

"Will you be there?"

"I'll do my best," Ditch Pollard said.

*

At first, it was only Laurie Pearl. And the photographs were formal, entirely innocent. She dropped the rolls off at the drugstore in the village. And a week or so later, the prints, fairly large, were returned. Later, it proved impossible to offer the negatives to the eyes of others. Laurie sent away to Rochester for chemicals, and he developed the negatives, and made prints in a makeshift darkroom in the house where he had been raised.

The equipment was not cheap. The Kodak film tank alone cost $6.50; the fixing and washing tank another $2.50. Then there were the powders, developers, fixers, developing clips, a darkroom lamp with a 5/8 inch wick. Where was she getting the money? Stealing it, she said. From her father.

Another commandment violated. He had passed the point of no return.

*

Callie had the habit of doing her business with the door flung wide for all the world to see. It was her way of establishing intimacy he thought. And to show her trust. And maybe deep down to flirt. Watching the child pee, her legs straddling the old wooden seat,

32

triggered a protectiveness in him. Nothing so vulnerable, he thought. Most of the women he could number in his life, they also sooner or later opened this door. He remembered Laurie Pearl, crouched in the grass in her father's high meadows, looking up at him, bold and shy at the same time, as if to say, see, I deny you no secrets.

"You wipin' the wrong way," he told the child. "Front to back, not back to front."

*

He was convinced her girlfriends had picked him because he could not tell. Because if he did, some outraged vigilante might put a bullet in his skull, the way he imagined his father had disappeared on Stone Mountain.

But in the beginning it was just Laurie, the girl unbuttoning the top button of her blouse. Just one button. Hell, that might have been all it took. She was not the smartest woman he would know in his long life. But about being female, no Cleopatra or Josephine could outdistance her. One button. It was more devastating than stepping naked out of the barn hay. One button. Filled with dizzying promise.

*

Calliope looked at him. Between them, there were always unspoken questions, operating on a wavelength denied to others.

"Thinkin' about being young," he said.

"Granma said when you were young, you were *a dog.*"

"Granma don't know nothin'."

"Says you were a *roguish fellow.*"

He pondered on that for a minute. "A dog and a rogue. Goes hand in hand, I guess."

"I saw your picture," Callie said. "Black nappy hair, all *over* your head. And you weren't bent over."

"I wasn't old," he said.

"I like you old," the child said. "I like you old. And I like the way you smell. You got kind of a buttery smell about you."

Ditch Pollard laughed out loud, then took a while to get back his breath.

Callie crawled into his lap, put her finger against his lips.

*

It was Laurie Pearl who had stopped his breath with her own. He had stood like a fool, his arms stiff at his sides, until she lifted his hands, and placed them against her face.

A week later, she took him to the settlement, that collection of twelve cabins built around the time of the Civil War the girl had said, buried deep in the woods, an abandoned place unknown to him, shaking his boy's confidence that he knew the territory of Slaters Ridge, every boulder and underground spring, and suddenly finding within a quarter mile of a road he walked daily a village within the village, cabins prim and proper marching in order down to a pond, an outhouse for each, set far enough back from the pond so as not to corrupt it and the well with its rusted iron pump and handle.

Laurie Pearl forced the old hinges of one of the cabins and drew him inside into a dankness that smelled like evil. He was fool enough to believe that God was watching, that fornication of any kind would command a terrible price, and that letting this white girl touch him in the way she was doing was preparing his place in hell.

*

The problem with being church-raised he thought was that instead of accommodating the forces at work in the world, you end up in a whirlwind of myth and superstition, a universe of opaque fogs and transparent illusion constructed by an all-seeing magician. Hell, his great-granddaughter's name was born of that same impulse, of myth and needs so old that the mysteries got told and retold, passed on from first generation to last, from continent to continent.

"I saw Miss Laurie Pearl in the village last week," Callie said.

"Do tell."

"She's so old," Callie said. "And mean. Like the witch that melted."

"You got to talk nice about people," the child's grandmother said from the kitchen. "So they'll talk nice about you."

It was not a life's lesson in which Ditch believed. He grunted his disapproval. The child followed his lead.

"Old white people don't look good," Callie said. "Miss Pearl looks kind of ashy and sick. And she talks like she got a coffee grinder stuck in her throat."

Callie's grandmother charged in from the kitchen. "What a terrible way to talk about people. Girl, you should show some respect."

Callie crawled onto Ditch's lap. "Poppa Ditch is beautiful," she said. "Like me."

"Girl is full of herself. You keep telling that child she's beautiful and someday there will be hell to pay."

"Always is," he said.

*

In the cabin, a moment after she touched him, he lost control and ejaculated into her hands.

"There now," Laurie Pearl said.

Then she did an extraordinary thing, lifting her hands to her nostrils, breathing in his scent. And then another extraordinary thing. Miss Laurie Pearl lifted her blouse and rubbed his semen into her belly.

Young fool that he was, he had always considered his ejaculate a kind of pollution. She seemed totally unaware of the danger in it.

"Next time," she said. "I want you to put yourself inside of me."

"Can't do it."

"Oh, I think you can."

The girl undid the buttons of her blouse, and moving her hands behind her back, undid the fastenings of her undergarment.

The nipples, pale pink, the color of her lips, stood straight out, pointing in his direction.

"I am getting so wet," she said. "My drawers are soaked."

As fearful as he was at that moment of God and of her father, Sam Pearl, who both seemed of a sudden to combine into one entity, his Johnson again came to awful and riotous attention. He had fantasized so long about Laurie Pearl's breasts. And there they were, the devil's toys, just a hand's length away.

*

"You thinking about old times," Callie said.

"How you know that?"

"You were smiling," she said. "With your eyes closed."

"I was laughing at myself," he said. "You get old, you get a lot of funny memories."

"You were dreamin'," Callie said.

*

At first, it was just the girls arranging themselves in what were suggestive positions—these school friends of Laurie Pearl's—in front of this black boy. He pretended to a professionalism that was patently fraudulent, selecting f-stops and shutter speeds according to the Kodak manual, setting the shutter by pressing lever E, exposing film by pressing lever C.

A few weeks later, the girls giggling and conspiring in one of the cabins at the settlement, lined up like dancers, their backs to him, then turned one by one to reveal their bared breasts.

The one named Myrna began pointing at his arousal. They asked to see what all the excitement was about. He fled the cabin. Left the camera for Laurie to retrieve.

*

A year later, in the back of Sam Pearl's barn, Laurie whispered to him that she was pregnant, carrying his child. Ditch wanted her to have his baby. They would go to Canada, he told her. Instead, she took the train to New York with Myrna. Myrna's boyfriend was a second-year medical resident. He knew about the goings-on in the cabin. The boyfriend had been invited up there. And had posed for some photographs with Myrna, photos that Ditch knew were buried under one of the buildings. It was Myrna's boyfriend who performed the abortion. And later became one of the two doctors serving Slaters Ridge.

Ditch's own opinion had never been asked.

"You killed my child," he said.

"Our child," Laurie Pearl said.

Ditch shook his head. "I never took you for a coward."

"Nigger, I was not afraid to have your child."

Ditch waved her off. He did not want to hear any of this hypocrisy.

"Me they would not kill," she said. "You, that's a different story."

He did not believe for a moment that she had destroyed the child in order to save his life. If the devil had taken the shape of a woman and descended on a mountain village, he had come as Laurie Pearl. Later Ditch had the courage to admit to himself that he was relieved. He was certain he would have broken his own mother's heart. And did not know until Molly Mintz had confessed it to him in what she knew to be her final days that Ditch's mother had known all along. The daughter of slaves up from Georgia had said to Molly that the white girl was not good enough for her son. And she had refused to tell him that Laurie Pearl was somehow his better, when she was not. Or that her son's Johnson was unworthy when it was not. Oh, dangerous it was. And probably unholy. But she was not about to kowtow to anybody. She had worked too hard, had been too infected with Molly Mintz's freethinking and her own Methodist Episcopal sense of herself to tell her son that these people they lived among were somehow superior.

Fact was her son deserved better than this white girl. She was not a Christian, for one thing. Was common for another. Next thing to a streetwalker.

*

Ditch Pollard never lay with Laurie Pearl again, never touched her or sought the comfort in her body. She would teach some other boy to make photographs, and one day Ditch would dig up the pictures buried in an old paint can up there in the settlement. But he was out of that game.

It would take a long lifetime before he would even consider trusting one of them again. Even Molly Mintz, whose color he often forgot, he could not, would not, trust with his soul. Always seemed to have some high-sounding motive. But sooner or later, if you let them, they killed what you loved. And they called you a name.

*

"You grinding your teeth," Callie said. "Again!"

He unfolded himself out of his sleeping chair, took Callie by the hand.

It was time to make their daily errand into the village. The two were a familiar sight, the skinny old black man, knees and elbows all knobs, and the fawn-colored child, driving him forward with her own elastic energy, passing the village's year-round Hasid families in their somber black dress, pausing to speak a few words of Yiddish here and there, the little girl's accent almost as good as his own. In her innocence and parochial world view, she believed that all black people moved through a sea of black-clad Jews, that the world itself was a flexible creation, changing shape and form, according to the language you used to address it, that food changed its taste depending on the word you used for it, that words that were bad in one language were often pleasantly disguised in another, and that politenesses varied, that some words and phrases curtsied while others danced.

Old-believers in black, newcomers speaking Spanish and Spanglish, were the girl's dictionary.

At the post office in the center of town, Ditch held Callie up to their box and she spun the combination with authority. Two letters only, a bill from the electric company and a solicitation from the NAACP, an organization he had favored ever since they had fought for an anti-lynch law in the 1930s.

*

From her window above the shuttered dry goods store, the crone, Laurie Pearl, saw Ditch Pollard parading through town with that great granddaughter of his, on his arm. The old woman determined to make it to the street to confront him with her sorrow.

*

In the store where he had worked half a century previous, a place once catering to secular Jews from eastern Europe, now re-named the Spanish-American Market, he and Callie picked out a crown roast of pork. The child probably would not eat it, but loved the look of it and believed it was appropriate to her own royal status. At age six, Ditch's princess-child had already mastered more than a few phrases of Yiddish, Hebrew, and Spanish. She thanked Mr. Eddie Hernandez in his native language for the bag of M&Ms he had conferred upon her. And then moved to the dry food shelf and selected two boxes of macaroni and cheese.

"I like what you did to the store," Ditch said. "Got some bright lights in here, finally. An old man can now see the merchandise which may or not be a boon to business.

"Seems like yesterday," Ditch said. "Place used to be filled with ladies spouting Yiddish, squeezing melons, sniffing the rear ends of fresh-killed poultry. Couple summers, one of the Pearls, Miss Laurie Pearl's nephew, her sister Alexandra's boy, worked with me here, picking orders for the bungalow colonies and hotels which in those days were still crowded with summer people. Old Studebaker truck. No sane man would drive a truck like that these days. Shake the kidneys loose from their moorings. But seemed good enough back then."

The boy had loved making deliveries in that old truck. They had more than once shared a swig from Ditch's bottle of rye whisky under the seat, and a cigarette or two along the way. He had been a good kid all in all, and seemed not to have been a victim of the craziness that afflicted most of the Pearl family. But Ditch never told the boy that he had once bedded down with the boy's aunt. And that the boy had lost a colored cousin to an abortionist's knife.

*

The wildness in the Pearl blood had been passed generation to generation. He had watched the growing up of Laurie Pearl's daughter, Rhoda, the red-headed child who several months pregnant had gone off to New York and married at eighteen, and in recent years had gotten herself a cancer.

She had returned just the year before, gaunt, hollow-eyed, to visit her mother. To Ditch's dim eyes Rhoda was still beautiful. But the pangs of guilt he felt about her persisted. He had in an oblique way led her to the photographs when she was just fifteen, using her cousin who helped him on the truck to set that all in motion. And had convinced himself that it was to protect her from the wildness, to disgust her and open her eyes to the evil around her. Instead, it had set her off. If he dared be honest about his motives, it was revenge on old Sam Pearl for his bigotry. And perhaps worse—retribution on Laurie Pearl for killing his child. He had manipulated so many lives, making himself more a god than old Calliope had been a goddess. So he had arranged for Rhoda to discover her mother's nakedness, the young Laurie Pearl captured by a Kodak Autographic playing the whore in one of the cabins of the settlement. And had set in motion events which eventually led to Rhoda's estrangement from the cousin whom she had loved.

He felt responsible even for Rhoda's cancer. When one corrupts another human being, he believed there might be no end to the corruption. Happy people don't get sick as much as the sad and depressed. If you created their unhappiness, then you bore a heavy responsibility.

*

Callie offered him an M&M.

God's justice was often confusing. Given his track record, he did not deserve the affection of this child. Yet, there it was, the crowning gift of his life. If only it could be accepted without harming any more of the world that seemed to revolve around him. Callie's mother was already a walking tragedy, whoring for drug money on the Brooklyn streets. He hoped that was the end of it. The end of divine payback for his own sins. And that the child, Callie, would be spared.

*

"Eat some more candies," Callie said. "Makes you walk faster."

Ditch smiled. They were approaching the dry goods store where Laurie Pearl had once worked, and above which she still lived. Callie wanted to pass the store as quickly as she could. Laurie Pearl was her bogeyman. Most of her nightmares involved Laurie. As did some of his.

"Miss Laurie Pearl," Ditch said, with a small nod. He held the child's hand tighter as the old woman appeared in the doorway.

"Gone," she said. "Gone."

"You lost something, Miss Pearl?"

"Dammit, Ditch. Don't play any fucking games with me."

"The child..." Ditch said.

Laurie Pearl turned to study Callie. "She's a girl. She'll be up to her neck in shit before she knows it." Laurie Pearl grabbed the door frame for support. "Rhoda's gone. Killed herself last night." The old woman sat down in the doorway, resting on the stone sill. Ditch knelt beside her. "We killed Rhoda," she said softly. "We killed my baby girl."

*

He had wanted to tell Laurie Pearl that every day he mourned his own living granddaughter, murdering herself in Brooklyn. But he dared not at that moment impose his own pain. In its suddenness, Laurie Pearl's pain was so pure it was impossible to share.

*

"What she mean?" Callie said as they walked back to the house.

"Just an old woman," Ditch said. "Her mind don't click together all the time."

"She an ugly old woman," Callie said.

"You can't be so quick to judgment when you lookin' at the remains of a person," Ditch said. "She was a little girl, just like you once. And a beautiful young woman. But you hang around long enough, you get car-wrecked, you know."

"You old," she said. "And you beautiful."

He knelt down to the little girl.

"I want you to remember all of your life how important you are."

*

Learning what to forgive, and what not to forgive is God's game, he thought. And one day your life's end has snuck up on you and if you are lucky to have lived long, and fortunate to have some of your intelligence still intact, you have the time to attempt to figure out the unfigurable. Somewhere out there in the universe is the spirit of his unborn son, a child the color of coffee corrupted with cream, and he wants to apologize to that child that he started him on his way and was not there to see him through. And now, there is Rhoda, set adrift by her own hand. What will he say the next time they meet? May you rest in peace, girl. May no country nigger come bearing photographic gifts,

41

intent on visiting your mother's sins upon your head.

And to Molly Mintz he will say: I was wrong not to trust you. But based on the evidence I had in hand, it was the right thing to do.

*

"I can't wake him up," Callie said.

"He's just playing," her grandmother said. "Just shake him gently."

The little girl and the old woman stood for a long time watching the rise and fall of his thin chest. Only Ditch Pollard knew he was beneath the Neversink, pursuing the muse with her cowrie shell braids.

"He's breathing good," the girl said.

"Too mean to die," her grandmother said. "Just an old dog. Chasin' his dinner in his dreams."

Calliope giggled. "He a rogue, all right." And then she laughed out loud.

Rusty Dolleman
Sheepdog

*T*he phone rings, and I'm not afraid. Not even when it's snowing and Patrick's late getting home from his shift, and I'm reminded that police officers can die in car accidents just as easily as they can on the job. I just cross the kitchen briskly, pick up the receiver without checking the caller ID, and when I hear Penny Fayette's Kentucky drawl I do not feel relief, because there is nothing to be relieved about.

"Hi Megan," Penny says. "Have you heard from Patrick?"

"Nope." I walk back into the living room, where my son is sitting on the couch, still playing his father's XBox. Aaron's not afraid of the phone either, and this is one of my greatest accomplishments as a mother.

"You haven't?"

"Nope."

"Well, that's funny."

Out with it, I think. Patrick was in court with Penny's husband today, and so I'm once again the back channel by which she can try to nail down Carl's whereabouts. "They're probably just doing paperwork," I say. "You know how it is."

"I sure do." Penny lets out a sad little laugh. "Carl has to work Christmas Eve *and* Christmas Day."

"That sucks." Leave him, I think. Penny's the head regional sales rep for a pharmaceutical company, and most of the money is hers. She also knows that even though police officers often have a lot of post-shift paperwork, this doesn't mean Carl isn't cheating on her. Therefore she's forced to fish around with these phone calls, hoping to snag some spare, rotten piece of information that will tell her once and for all *yes he is* or *no he's not,* and it's my job to not confirm anything either way. I can't tell her, for example, that Carl actually has Christmas Eve off, and I don't want to, either. As far as I'm concerned, Penny Lafayette can figure these things out for herself.

"Well, give me a call if you hear anything, all right?"

"Sure." I lean over, turn on the outside lights, my sweater stretching tight over my stomach. My clothes have begun to not fit quite right again, and there's something almost pleasant about this, like a sore muscle. My bulbs begin their crazy twinkle, and I think of Penny's Christmas lights, those soft stately white candles in each window of that huge house on the other side of the city.

I go back into the living room, stand next to where Aaron's sitting. Apparently, I'm in his way, because he grunts, slides a couple inches to the side. I don't think he even understands the game, his Tom Clancy spy doesn't even come close to the Columbians or Tajiks or whoever this particular mission calls upon you to "neutralize." Instead, Aaron just runs into corners and falls off ledges, the black-suited figure on the screen breathing heavily whenever one of the terrorists gets in one of their own whacks.

"Do I make a better door than a window?" I ask. This is something his father says to me, an inside-the-family joke.

"Yes," Aaron says.

"Do you even know what you're doing?" The spy sets off an alarm, and his head—which has some bizarre three-pronged apparatus mounted on it—whips from side to side in animated panic. "What's that on his face?"

"A camera." My son's voice is already tinged with that same tired frustration his father gets when he has to explain what he thinks should be obvious. But I'm the one who's sat Aaron down in front of the TV, so I can't really complain. When he's finally killed and the *Mission*

'Writing fiction works best for me when I remind myself that it's one of the many human endeavors that's best viewed as a process, rather than a means by which we hope to achieve a certain outcome (literary success, producing a certain "type" of story, etc). To paraphrase Richard Bausch, the only question writers should ask themselves is "Did I work today?"'

~ Rusty Dolleman

Failed screen comes up, I navigate through the menus for him, restart the game.

After a few minutes, Penny calls again. "Carl's not answering his cell phone," she says. "I think something's wrong."

"Do you want me to call Patrick?"

"I hate to make you do that."

"I'll call you back." I hang up the phone before she can say thank you, dial Patrick's number. It's one thing for Carl to lie to his wife, it's another to avoid her entirely, make her think he's plastered all over the highway somewhere.

When my husband answers, it's in the voice he only dares to use when he's stuck at the station, the one that suggests I'm still too stupid to realize that the less I call, the quicker he'll be able come home.

"What?" he says.

"Hello to you too," I say. "Penny called. Twice."

"Well, don't let her get her hooks into you." Now that he knows this call isn't about *his* being late, his tone has loosened into sympathy.

"Is Carl there?"

"Unfortunately, Officer Fayette is unavailable for the moment." This means Carl is at Killarney's with his girlfriend, a state trooper named Jessica who was in Patrick's class at the academy. "Would you like to leave a message for him?"

"Tell him his wife called." Patrick promises he will, and before he hangs up, he tells me he loves me. When I call Penny back, her phone is busy, and so I sit and wait, listen to the tapping of my son's fingers, the foreign shouts of computerized guards on alert, and wonder how it is that I've actually come to feel sorry for this woman.

*

The first time my husband brought his service weapon home, I was surprised by how dull and gray and ordinary it looked. It was more like something out of a Black and Decker catalogue than the sleek and shiny pistols I'd seen in the movies, and when I mentioned this to Patrick, he said yes, that's how I should think of it, as a tool, a highly specialized piece of equipment designed for one specific task. Then he put both the gun and the rag he'd been cleaning it with in a shoebox on the top shelf of our closet and fell face-first onto the bed.

The department had started him off on the midnight shift, and his life was divided between times he struggled to stay conscious and times he had to force himself into sleep. When he was awake, we'd fight. We ended up going to the Fayette's Labor Day party mostly because we thought being around other people would make us less likely to spend the afternoon at each other's throats.

Since Carl had already been on the force for a few years, the Fayettes no longer had to live within the city limits. The houses in their neighborhood all had stone paths snaking through the lawns, shaded entryways and stone chimneys, the kind of places Patrick and I had both grown up in and always assumed we'd live in ourselves. Instead, we were sweating it out in a downtown apartment complex, and I was kicking myself for insisting Patrick take the job that would keep us closest to our families instead of those town-cop jobs up in the mountains, places where he would've spent most of his time pulling skiers with out-of-state plates over for speeding and pulling drunks out of snowbanks.

When we arrived, Carl was standing in his backyard with his daughter on his shoulder, his other hand dripping with lobster parts. He was shirtless, the thickness of his body just beginning to melt into fat

46

around his waist. Patrick, right? he said. Glad you could make it. Hope you brought a towel, beer's in the cooler. Later, after Patrick and I had drunk too much to drive, we were in the handful of people left around the picnic table, all of us listening to Carl's stories about being a cop in South Carolina. Since I was the only woman left—other than Penny— he directed the worst of it my way, all that talk about entrance wounds and crack whores and "nigger-be-nice" sticks, trying to shock me, trying to turn me on, probably. He was so intent on me that he didn't seem to notice that Patrick was transfixed by his own wife.

Or maybe he just didn't care. Carl must've known that none of those Yankee boys had ever seen anything like Penny. She was sitting down at the end of table in a blue-and-white sundress, running her own commentary on his stories, keeping all the other men in stitches. Oh, Carl, that's such *bullllllshit*, she'd say, making bullllllshit sound like the sexiest thing in the world, as if she'd just said "making love" instead. And what do you do, honey, Penny asked, sweeping her red hair back from her face.

I teach math, I said.

That's great. High school?

Middle school, Patrick answered for me.

We should give *you* a gun, Carl said.

No kidding, Penny said. Get 'em before they start. At this point Patrick put his arm around me, but I knew what he was thinking. If this was what it took to be a city cop's wife, I'd never make it.

To tell the truth, I hadn't done much to make him think otherwise. When the black-and-blue marks had begun appearing on his skin, raining down his ribs and thighs, I'd wondered aloud how the boy I'd known since high school could be out there mixing it up on the streets. Your poor, poor body, I said, and whenever he came home needing to talk about some car crash decapitation he'd seen that day, some little kid running around naked through rooms with dog shit on the floor, I'd remind him of our earlier, shared dream of his teaching phys ed in the same school where I worked. You could take classes this fall, I'd say. Just give yourself the option, at least.

Are you fucking kidding me? Patrick would reply. His teeth would be clenched, his body rigid in the bed next to mine. Do you really think this is why I'm telling you this shit? So you can give me permission to *quit*?

*

Even before I see the shape of the vehicle in the driveway, I know whose it is, and when I answer the door, Penny doesn't move, not even to take her hands from the pockets of her coat. Her truck is still running, the high beams still aimed at my kitchen windows. "I know you know something," she says.

"I don't know anything." Behind me, I hear Aaron slide off the couch, his controller clattering to the floor, and so I walk out onto the steps, close the door behind me. There's no one else in the truck, and I wonder where Penny's daughter is right now.

"Don't fuck around with *me*, Megan." She says it like I fuck around with other people all the time.

"He's at the station. I just talked to Patrick five minutes ago."

"I thought you said you didn't know anything."

This is it, I tell myself, this is the last time I run interference for Carl Fayette. But I know that's not true. The first time I met Carl's girlfriend, Jessica had hugged me without warning, began talking about how she'd been partnered with Patrick during pepper-spray training at the academy. It was so nice to go through that with a guy who didn't need to act all tough, she said, and Jessica's still the only female officer who's genuinely happy when I make one of my rare appearances at the bar. The only one who, cop or no cop, acknowledges that we are two women with a man in common, and that we can be friends. The rest of them barely speak to me, and I can tell they're all disappointed Patrick and I haven't split up yet. Squealing on Carl means squealing on Jessica, and I won't do it. "God, Penny, what is this?" I fold my arms, make my teeth chatter. "Give me a break."

Penny stares at me for a moment, then begins walking back to her truck. This isn't for show, she's really going to leave humiliated, having gotten nothing in return for her accusation, and she'll never be able to call me again, neither as a friend nor a fellow sufferer.

"Penny wait." I follow her down the steps and into the snow, the red and green Christmas lights reflecting in the silver trim of my gym sneakers.

She turns around with a look of weary suspicion. "What do you want, Megan?" she asks, and I can feel my gut unwinding as I realize what I'm about to do. It will only be a furthering of the lie, for one thing, but I don't see any other way to respond and still call myself a human being.

"I swear to God I don't know anything," I say. "Please come in."

Penny sniffs, clears her throat, and for a moment I think she's going to lay into me, say *I know you've always hated me, you must love this,* but then she opens, reaches into her truck, turns the engine off.

We walk back to the house without speaking, but when I push the door open, Aaron is standing right there, so close that I almost knock him over. His little pink face looks so lost and lonely that Penny has to laugh.

"Oh no, Aaron," she says, "Where did Mommy *go?*" She laughs again when he tries to duck between my legs and the row of cabinets beneath the counter. "He's so shy," Penny says.

"Only around people he doesn't know," I say.

"Alicia's at a friend's tonight." She sits down at the kitchen table, waits as I make coffee. "I guess I just got lonely or something."

It's hard for me to picture Alicia with friends. As far as I can tell, Penny's daughter is herself practicing to be a mute, and I wonder why they decided against having any more children. One of them, at least, must have come to the conclusion that, given the current situation, it's probably for the best, and now poor Alicia will have to grow up dealing with all of this by herself. I'm reminded again of how lucky I am, not only to have two parents who live close-by and still love each other, but four older siblings as well. If any kind of rupture had occurred, my brothers and sisters would've formed a phalanx around me, and that's why I pushed to have another baby now, before Aaron gets too old. I don't believe in only children.

When the coffee's ready, I lower myself into the seat across from Penny, pull Aaron onto my lap. He leans forward, starts running his fingers across the tabletop and pushing the placemats up against one another, and I draw him backward, against the familiar newness of my stomach. "Stop it," I say, and then we play the game where I try to bind two of his hands together with one of mine, and I lose. "Do you want me to call Patrick?" I ask.

"Oh, I'm fine," Penny says. "How far along are you?"

"Four months."

Penny nods, lifts her cup to her lips with both hands. It doesn't bother me that, sitting there in her long coat and clutching her coffee, wisps of red hair plastered against her cheek, Penny looks more beautiful than I do on my best days. It's that knowing smile, that soft, slow tone of voice, as if she's a woman in some elemental way that I'm not. Her coming here is part of this, and now that the jealous queen has mastered herself, she is going to hold court here in this simple schoolteacher's house.

"How've you been feeling?" she asks.

"Fine."

"Has Patrick told you about what's happening in court?"

"No," I say. "I don't like to hear about that stuff." This isn't true anymore, and I actually know quite a bit about this particular case. A pregnant woman had called the station to complain about her boy-friend. He'd spent the last six hours kicking her ass, she'd said, but then when they'd tried to arrest him, she'd bitten through the sleeve of Carl's uniform. Then she'd bit her own lip and tried to spit on the wound, claiming she had hepatitis. Then she'd intentionally shit her pants in the back of Carl's cruiser. But if it makes Penny feel better to think I'm some little kid, I'll play along.

"You don't want to, believe me. Everybody hates cops, you know?"

No, I think, even as my mouth makes its sympathetic *hmmmm*, everybody hates cops like Carl. This is the first time Aaron's heard that someone might hate his father, and even though I can't tell if the comment registered with him or not, I could still kill Penny for saying it. Up until now, Aaron's Dad has been someone who helps people, who makes bad men stop, and I don't want to have to explain about how sometimes even the people the bad men are hurting hate his father.

You know what I think? Patrick said the night after they'd arrested the pregnant woman. I think people deserve what they get. And you know what else? I think I might actually be an evil person for thinking this. By now I've learned not to even hint that he should give up being a police officer—since this is what he calls himself, refusing to even let the word "cop" be said in his presence—but I still think it. Yes, I think, you've done your best, you're good at your job, you can handle yourself. Now *quit*.

Aaron leans forward, spilling himself in half over my arms. "You know what?" I say, letting him go. "I'm going to call Patrick again. I just don't want Carl to be worried if he gets home and wonders where you are." I hug the phone to my shoulder, avoiding Penny's eyes, and when Patrick picks up, I let him know through every code of our secret language that Carl is to stop whatever it is he's doing, come over here and get his wife out of my house.

*

There was a time, though, when even being a police officer wasn't enough. A few of the guys on the force are ex-military, and for a while Patrick was considering joining the Marines. Maybe he really hadn't done his part, he reasoned, maybe he'd be a better police officer, a better person, if he did just one four-year bid. It was as if he honestly thought he could put himself in harm's way, move himself across the ocean to places where human life was a million times cheaper than on even the worst street in Manchester, and that I'd have to sit and take it, if only to make up for the fact that I'd once doubted he was cut out for law enforcement. For the first time, I began to think about *divorce*, to rehearse ways of explaining to my family and friends why Patrick and I were ending a ten-year relationship when I was pregnant and we'd just bought a house, ways that wouldn't include admitting that the baby's conception was the only time we'd had sex that entire fall, or that my husband was leaving me because he thought I was a wimp. Or that I was leaving him because I was tired of being thought of in this way.

That spring, the hornets that had spent the winter sleeping in our walls began to wake up, and when I came home from school, there'd be at least one on each windowsill. A half-dozen more would be roaming the ceiling and walls, and I couldn't even sit down or even pick up a newspaper without first examining every inch of every surface I was about to come into contact with. I even found one in the bed once, and so I took to sleeping in long pants, terrified that one would crawl up my thigh in the night, sting me awake. At first, Patrick just laughed, but then he began to get annoyed. Just vacuum them up, for Christ's sake, he'd say. Or at least trap them in a glass so I can get rid of them when I get home. He had bigger things to worry about, he said, and one night we'd lain awake as he'd explained how, if a certain likely event occurred in one Central Asian country, it could very well bring about a change in a neighboring country's upcoming elections, inflaming a specific ethnic group in an outlying province and starting an Islamic revolution in Pakistan. The end result would be that the Muslims would have a nuclear weapon, and Patrick was staring at the ceiling, ticking off what would happen next until I thought I would scream. So that means you should join the Marines? I said.

Well, someone's got to do something. Someone's got to be worry about it.

Hey, I'm worried. I'm worried for two.

Oh, that's right, he exploded. Only you care about the baby. I don't care about him at all.

Evidently not, if you're going to join the Marines.

There are wolves, there are sheep, and there are sheepdogs. Patrick was saying this quite a bit back then, usually in his weariest of voices, and predicating it with *There are three types of people in this world.* It was a cop thing, for sure.

Oh, fuck you.

Don't worry about it. He turned onto his side, away from me, clutched his pillow to his face. You just keep those hornets under wraps and we'll be all set.

I didn't say anything after that. I just lay there in the darkness, not waiting for an apology, or even for my anger to subside. In fact, I realized I was feeling the way men must feel when they've finally had enough, just can't stop themselves from taking a swing at the woman they claim to love. When I knew Patrick was asleep, I reached down between his legs, took the skin of his inner right thigh between my fingers and twisted, the only time I'd ever tried to physically hurt another human being.

He was over me in a second, with his knees. What the fuck was that?

A hornet. I went to pinch him again, but he slapped my hand away, grabbed both of my wrists and forced them onto the bed. For a moment we stayed that way, my stomach rising up between our bodies, and then he jumped off the bed, went into the bathroom and slammed the door.

When I went in fifteen minutes later, he was still sitting on the toilet with the lid down, his elbows on his knees. Did you come in here so you wouldn't hit me? I asked, but he didn't answer or even look at me. You know what? I took a step closer. If there was a big nuclear war and my Mom and Dad were dead and your parents were dead and our son's face got melted off and there was no more United States, I still wouldn't let you join the goddamned Marines. What I didn't say was *because then we wouldn't be together, and that's all I really care about.* I wasn't sure if this was really true anymore, and I didn't want to give him any excuse to act like this was another instance where he had to be "strong for both of us," either.

His face wouldn't really melt off, Patrick said. He wasn't smiling, but it looked as if he might, in an moment. That's not what happens with acute radiation poisoning.

You know what I mean. I swayed a little, not in a sexy way, but as if I *had* been hit, a physical acknowledgement that all the things I'd just said might very well come to pass. They were already happening, in a way, right there in the bathroom, we were already dying, radioactive snow flying out of a dark yellow sky, and I wanted to climb on top of him and fuck, fuck, fuck, but I knew I wouldn't. We hadn't had sex since I'd become pregnant either, and I was afraid of how impersonal it would seem, as if it really were the last time. I could feel the fight beginning to end, and I knew that if we just waited a few days, it would feel like us again.

Do you know what happens with acute radiation poisoning?

No, I said, I don't, and for once he didn't tell me.

*

Now Patrick is walking through the door, and Carl is coming behind him, kicking the snow off his boots and smiling like Santa Claus himself. "Hello, hello," he says, but when he looks at me, the smile turns into a jeer. I can imagine the conversation that must've taken place at Kilarney's, Carl trying to brush Patrick off, Patrick remaining calm but insistent, refusing to leave until Carl paid for his tab and stood up, swearing bitterly the whole time. Jessica would've been pushing him out the door as well, her own anger directed more at herself than at Penny, and probably still at the bar now, wondering how her life had gotten to be this way, dating a married man who doesn't even treat his wife *well.*

"Oh my God," Penny stands up slowly, as if she doesn't know whether she should fly into Carl's arms or find the sharpest knife in the counter-rack. "What are you doing here?"

"Oh, nothing." Carl stands in the center of the room, beaming as if he's saying, *I thought of it myself. I wanted to come here and surprise you. I love you, you know.* At that moment, Aaron comes into the kitchen, and Patrick lays one open palm down at his side, inviting him to come over and rub his head against it like a cat.

"What's up, bud?" Patrick asks, and Aaron's response is lost as he mashes his face against his father's pants. They're so happy to see one another, they've missed each other so much, and I can feel the jealousy kicking in, thin and sick and bitter. But I don't want to be mad at them, I want to be mad at Carl, so I leap to my feet, clap my hands together.

"It's a Christmas Miracle," I say. Patrick gives me a look, and Carl's smile freezes on his face.

"Megan," he says. "Meg, Meg, Megan."

"Yes?" I ask. It's okay with me if Carl Fayette hates my guts. It really is. Even as I keep his secrets.

"I got..." Aaron holds up three fingers to his face, stretches his cheek with one of them. "I got to level three."

"You did?" Patrick asks, his face suddenly one of intense interest, but when he looks at me, I shake my head. I don't think the game Aaron was playing even *has* levels.

"Carl come on," Penny says. She takes a step forward, puts her hand on Carl's shoulder.

"What a nice little house." Carl swivels his head, makes a show of looking around the kitchen. "You're kind of a little princess around here, aren't you?"

"Sure am." I bat my eyelashes at him. "I've got my crown upstairs."

"Get your way a lot, I bet."

"Oh, every time. I run my husband ragged."

"I know." Carl nods. He's not smiling anymore. "I know you do."

"Carl, let's *go.*" Penny pushes her husband, but she's unable to force his body into even the shadow of a movement. He flicks her arm away without even looking in her direction, and out of the corner of my eye I see Patrick softly push Aaron toward the living room, begin to shake his jacket off. His eyes never leave the back of Carl's head, and I stifle the urge to laugh out loud. Carl's half a foot taller than Patrick, and significantly wider. If I do goad Carl into crossing some sort of line, I'm not quite sure what he plans to do about it, especially with Aaron hanging all over him. But this doesn't make me want to stop. In fact it only makes me want to keep going. Let's do it, I think, let's find out once and for all who's the toughest, who's the most callous. Fuck this fucking around.

"What can I tell you?" I say. "I'm high maintenance. I want my husband to come home after work every night."

Carl opens his mouth, winding up again, but before he can respond, Penny opens the kitchen door. "This is so stupid," she says, then walks out by herself.

For a moment, Carl glowers at me. Then, all at once, his entire body seems to sag, as if he's just realized that without his wife in the room, he's just a man standing in the kitchen of somebody else's house, unwanted and getting in the way of dinner. "Thanks a lot, Megan," he says.

"Don't blame me," I say. "Just answer your phone when your wife calls."

He doesn't say anything else, or even look at Patrick. He just leaves. As the door closes, Aaron begins to cry, and Patrick scoops him up, shakes his head at me. Not angrily, not even in a bewildered sort of way, but the way you shake your head at someone who's done something you don't totally agree with but can't help but admire.

"Never heard Mommy talk that way before, huh buddy?" he asks, and Aaron buries his red, screaming face, the one that seems to get narrower every day, into his shoulder. His answer comes as a long, grating scream, an absurdly drawn out *No-oo-oo-oo-oo* that makes us both laugh.

*

Later in bed, I ask Patrick about what happened in court.

"Not much." He laughs, remembering. "She said she had diarrhea and we wouldn't let her use the bathroom."

"Did she?" It's not inconceivable that such a thing could happen, especially with Carl, or that Patrick would choose to not tell me about it. But when he turns over, he looks disgusted that I would even ask.

"I saw her face. She went like this." He clenches his teeth in an exaggerated pantomime of someone trying to go to the bathroom, glares at me with a hatred so comical that I'm surprised he's capable of replicating it.

"No," I say, laughing. "She didn't look like that."

"Oh yes, she did." Patrick makes the face again, and I laugh so hard that I begin hiccupping. He waits for me to calm down before sliding his arms around me, and I can tell by the thoughtful expression on his face that he's thinking about my little stand-off with Carl Fayette. "Mama Sheepdog," he says, and I don't know if it's his words or the way he pulls me to him—rough and playful, almost sexless—that brings the anger glittering back to the surface.

"Don't call me that," I snap, and I turn over onto my back. After a moment, he shifts his body downward, lays his head lightly on my stomach. I let him stay there, run my hand once through his hair, all the apology I can manage.

New Millennium Writings

Is pleased to present the New Millennium

Nonfiction Awards

Winning entries appear on pages 58-83

Summer 2008
Katharine Goodridge Ingram, Ojai, CA
Swimming Under Salvador, 58

Winter 2008-09
Melanie M. Hoffert, Minneapolis, MN
The Allure of Grain Trucks, 68

HONORABLE MENTIONS

Summer 2008	*Winter 2008-09*
Adrienne Amundsen, San Francisco, CA	Patricia Bjorklund, Wilmington, NC
Dawn-Michelle Baude, Goult, France	Marcia Corbino, Sarasota, FL
Joni Bour, Florence, OR	Adaeze Elechi, Nashville, TN
Julie Dalberg, Missoula, MT	Harrison Fletcher, Denver, CO
Edward Feldman, Sebastopol, CA	Sandra Giles, Tifton, GA
Molly Greeley, Halethorpe, MD	Linda Henry, White Bear Lake, MN
Gilda Haber, Silver Spring, MD	Sarah Heston, Columbia, MO
Eson Kim, Stratford, NJ	Michelle Lanzoni, Missoula, MT
Sigrun Kuefner, Missoula, MT	Mitchell Levenberg, Brooklyn, NY
John Malone, Waynesville, NC	Jeremy Lloyd, Townsend, TN
George Newtown, Benton, LA	Derek Lyons, Los Angeles, CA
Linda Overman, Encino, CA	A Marzano-Lesnevich, Cambridge, MA
Alice Owens Johnson, Black Mountain, NC	Kathryn Pauli, Shanghai, China
Elizabeth Porter, Tucson, AZ	Carol Perehudoff, Toronto, Ontario
Kaitlin Puccio, Montgomery, NY	Iraj Isaac Rahmim, Houston, TX
Renee G. Rivers, Phoenix, AZ	Karen Riley, Santa Fe, NM
Gabrielle Selz, Southampton, NY	Carole Sink, New York, NY
William Siavelis, Chicago, IL	Emily Williamson, Seattle, WA
Deborah Thompson, Fort Collins, CO	Jason Willits, Omaha, NE
Daniel D. Tomcheff, Portland, OR	Laura Esther Wolfson, New York, NY

Katharine Goodridge Ingram
Swimming Under Salvador

You and I are one.
You shield me from the sun
and fish me from the sea.
You belong to me.

Mama has planned the excursion. We are going from Mexico City to the hot springs of Cuautla, south of Cuernavaca. No. Daddy is not going. I don't hear all the reasons, but Mama is mad because she waited for him all night and he didn't come back, so Daddy is staying home.

I saw the three suitcases that fit into each other and look like one until he fills them with books for their rare book business. He just came back from Guatemala with old, yellow Spanish volumes covered in sheepskin. This time it will be New York.

"The children are going," Mama says. That means my brother and me and our friend from across the street, Chava, which is the nickname for his whole name, Salvador, just like his father. I don't hear the reasons, but his mother is not going either. She screams at her husband even though he is a famous sculptor. It's a high red scream with white fingernails in her mouth for teeth. Her green eyes are too bright and her hair is painted orange. When she cleans her house she puts a bandana around her head and ties it like a gypsy. Then she leaves rough, damp cloths spread out like rugs at every door in the house and tells us not to get her floors dirty. Across the street at Don Chucho's store, "La Malinche," they say she's *zafada* to wash her marble floors on her knees when there are girls right around the corner who would do it for a few pesos.

'I get the greatest energy and ideas from ART. A trip to the museum births characters and poems. Reading other authors is confirmation that we need each other. Advice that hurts belongs in the freezer for a month. Good advice should be noted, even taken, but only after leisurely consideration. A writers group of like-minded people, is invaluable for affirmation, encouragement, critique, and to keep a writer honest: that is, writing AND submitting. Stranded in a desert airport? Let me have at least Julio Cortázar and Gabriel García Márquez.'

~ Katharine Goodridge Ingram

There is no heart in her long white body, except when she bathes her boy Chava. Right after the bath, she wraps him up in a big white towel and sits him down on a bench with cushions. He's six. I'm five and she thinks I am so little that it's all right for me to watch. She doesn't know who sees out of me. She thinks I'm nobody. She dries her boy with the towel, then she takes out a tub of talcum powder with a round white velvet puff. She smoothes powder on him, moving the puff around on his body, on the back and the front. With two long white fingers she picks up his *pajarilla*, his little caterpillar—that's what Pilar calls it when my brothers are in the bath and their two pink caterpillars are bobbing in the water—and Chava's mother powders under it and pats his little lavender sack. It is wrinkled like a walnut with a raised seam between the halves. She dusts it and puts his worm back down on it. She powders his thighs and lifts his arms, ragdoll limp, to spin the powder puff in his armpits. Then his neck, his toes. I learned to powder the newborn baby next door. I didn't know you would powder a large boy with no diapers. Something in her is calm. Her eyes ride all over his skin.

Chava sits like a doll on the towel. He looks like the naked chickens Pilar props on the kitchen sink, washing them inside and out, rubbing lemon on them and drying them. He is not fun and mischievous the way he is with my brother. There is nothing in his eyes. He is like a tired dog waiting for his bath to be over. The white towel covers the bench and stretches over the floor like spilled milk. At last his mother pulls up the corners of it and wraps him. I think she wants to pick him up and carry him to his room, but she lets him walk by himself. I can go too and wait while she dresses him. She sits him on a bench of dark green leather under the window covered in vines. She pulls a thin white sock over one foot and then the other, smoothing the sock like a skin, her hand passing under his arch, over the instep and up the ankle, stopping as if she doesn't want to stop. She puts his undershirt over his head, pulling his arms through like the arms of a baby. Then his sweater and pants. He doesn't even have to tie his shoes himself. The thin leather is caked with white polish.

Afterwards, he and I go down the corridor toward the garden where the sun leaks through tall vines onto ferns and the red bricks of the walk are covered with bright green moss. We march like soldiers to the gate and out onto the damp yellow earth of the street. After the gate closes, we run to where my brother Primo is waiting on his bicycle, and we dash screaming down to the corner to "La Malinche." I jump when the side door opens. I think it is La Malinche* herself, mummified, electrified, come to live at the house with Her Name on it, her black hair turned grey from too many years with Cortés. But it is only Chucho's mother who's never supposed to be let out. We buy *paletas Mimí,* our favorite suckers of burnt sugar. We rough up Chava's perfectly combed hair, kick dirt on his heels and step all over the white toes of his thin shoes. Chava grabs my brother's bicycle and jumps on it backwards. Making clown faces, he rides wobbling down the street to the wrought-iron gates of our house.

Editor's Note—La Malinche (c. 1496 or c. 1505 – c. 1529, some sources give 1550), known also as Malintzin, Malinali or Doña Marina, was a woman (almost certainly Nahua) from the Mexican Gulf Coast, who played an active and powerful role in the Spanish conquest of Mexico, acting as interpreter, advisor and intermediary for Hernán Cortés. She was also a mistress to Cortés and gave birth to his first son, who is considered one of the first Mestizos (people of mixed European and indigenous American ancestry). In Mexico today, La Malinche remains iconically potent. She is understood in various and often conflicting aspects, as the embodiment of treachery, the quintessential victim, or simply as symbolic mother of the new Mexican people....

—From Wikipedia, entry on La Malinche.—DW

*

Once, Mama asked Chava's mother to paint Primo's portrait. Then Mama asked her to make my portrait. Her paintings are famous. Not as famous as her husband's sculptures, but big cars with chauffeurs bring people to her house to be painted.

The day of the portrait Mama walked with me across the street to leave me with Chava's mother.

"*Dios de mi vida*," she said, staring at my head near Mama's waist. "Look at her eyes. What color are they? Don't worry. Maybe she'll be beautiful like you someday."

I followed her to the studio at the back of the house and sat down facing the window on the chair with painted flowers. I looked out at the garden through the small panes of glass set from floor to ceiling. The trees had wet, twisted black trunks. But their blood came out in new green leaves. Primo and Chava and I knew how to skate and leave snake marks on the moss when no one was home. I wanted to look far away through the branches to what made shadows move.

"Over here!" she said, moving her thumb in the air to make me turn my head. I looked at her without blinking. She sat in a leather chair with green cushions, and her long green gown of silk poured like water down to the floor. A small canvas was already on the easel. She stuck her thumb through the hole in a round sheet of wood. It was covered with coils of paint as if birds had flown in and squirted out a dozen different colors. She took brushes from a bottle and stuck them in her fingers under the board of paint. She took another brush, held it, looked at it and then at me. She stared. I stared, trying to see her as a mother, an eye, a person. But she was made of thick glass and there was no way in. I waited stone still. Suddenly she screamed, "I cannot paint those eyes! I cannot paint those yellow eyes! Get out!" She threw a handful of brushes at me and I ran home.

Later she asked Mama for a photo and she painted me from that. When Mama brought it home she said, "This isn't a real portrait. It's not a likeness if you don't sit for it," and she gave it to my nurse Pilar, and Primo's portrait too. We both hang in Ixtapalapa in the large room where Pilar's sisters sleep. The little girl in the painting has two long, brown braids over her ears. Crooked bangs come down to her gold eyes. Her face is there, but there's no one inside her. She looks out into Pilar's room in the village where Pilar takes us sometimes, even though she really lives at our house, in a small room off the kitchen.

*

Big Salvador is going to the springs at Cuautla. Mama says he studied in Paris with Maillol, and now his women lie in large bronzes at the edges of gigantic fountains. His figures, smoothed and polished by his hands, rinsed and gleaming under sprays of water, are goddesses at the crossroads of the wide *avenidas* of Mexico City. They sit at the tops of marble steps, their gold breasts pressed between long, round arms. The city is like his own sculpture garden. I saw one of them in his studio. The enormous room was full of clay figures, wax miniatures and bronzes ready to polish. I saw the beautiful white woman he was carving in marble. She was alive. The stone glowed. The breasts were like skin filled with water pulling toward the ground. One thigh, lying heavy on the other, was soft. Even though it was not her face, I knew that inside her, in the neck, in the shiny bones of the knees, was my Mama.

Salvador is special. I don't remember his voice but I remember his body. He let me lean against his firm belly, his soft gray sweater on my face when Primo and Chava were mean to me in his car. I didn't tattle when they pulled my neck hairs because then his red-hair wife would turn around with her eyes of green ice. I knew that if I said anything, the white nails of her teeth would slice out of her beautiful face and bite me. When the car stopped and the door opened, I fell against Salvador. The boys ran off. I hugged his soft gray tower then ran home with my notebook where Miss Galindo makes us write *ajo, ojo, eje,* even though Daddy already taught me to read and to copy words on his typewriter.

*

Mama has packed a picnic. There is something distant and excited in her. In the car she and Big Salvador sit in front and I have to sit in back with Primo and Chava, but I get a window and don't have to sit between them. Today the boys are laughing and punching each other and they leave me alone.

The spa is covered with trees. The hot volcanic waters come out of a white grotto and spill over gray-white rocks into pools strung on steaming rivers descending the hill. The eucalyptus and pepper trees trail their long leafy arms in the blue pools.

Water rushes in the river, speeding faster and faster as it goes downhill. A leaf drops. We run along on the mossy edges following it. We can see it caught up by the water, spun, swallowed, thrown against a blue-white rock and stuck, then washed back into the deep and out of sight, gone, faster than we can run.

Mama has picked a middle pool with a wide grassy lap that spreads out under the pepper trees. She lets the wind loft a teal green cloth and then she lowers it to the ground. She takes two whole roasted chickens out of the basket. The aroma of fried onions comes out of a tall paper bag still steaming from the rotisserie on Insurgentes. The bread from "La Malinche" is sour two-pointed *bolillos* like tiny feet. Pilar has stuffed them with sweet butter. They are crisp outside, and white as cotton inside. Mama is serving Salvador. She pulls off a slab of breast the same size as the roll and slips it onto the butter. She adds a handful of shredded, deep-fried onions. Before she passes it to him, she wipes her hands clean on a big white napkin. I don't think they see us. Primo and Chava and I grab drumsticks and *bolillos* and run through the trees to the river. The water is clear. We stare at rocks below the blue stream. Above us we hear the yelps of the people trying the hottest water straight out of the grotto. Below we hear the cooing of those resting in the cooler pools.

The boys play games in the trees. They don't want to play with a girl. Under the trees the shade is too cold. I go where I want to be, by the edge of the warm water to feel the river that rises up the side of the grainy white rock, lifting lips of waves at my skin. It runs its hands over my feet and over my legs. It spins hot and firm around my calf, pushing and turning, rising to the knee, pulling me, wanting to bathe me and hold me. It comes higher on my thigh. It is so clear on the bottom that I can see each grain of sand around the rocks. I want to reach down and bring up one small stone just for me. I bend forward and reach in as far as I can.

It's too deep. I can't touch the stones and I can't hold onto the edge. The water tips me, turns me, swallows me.

I cry out, but I am pulled and swept away. I'm upside down. I come up just before the river pours itself over and begins its fall, the riverstretch to the next pool. I cry out again but I choke, and now I'm in the long, straight part of the river. I don't close my eyes. I think of Pilar praying about death to Our Lady — *ahora y en la hora de nuestra muerte, amen.* I watch with my eyes open. All the froth and bubbles like the flowered skeleton of La Calaca, La Muerte, with her wide-brimmed hat flapping over her hollow skull. And Pilar in my head saying, "See? *¿Ves? ¿Quién te lo manda?* Who told you to do such a thing?" The warm blue water twists me and throws me. Then I am face down. My arms and hands flail. I hit rocks and swirls and turns and deeps. When my head comes up through the water, I yell.

Suddenly I see Salvador running on the bank beside me. The river turns and plays. He runs straight along the edge but he can't keep up. He calls to me and I turn my eyes against the rolling of my neck to see him, to keep him with me. Please don't stop. Please don't stop running. He sees me. He's coming. But the river teases me to the other side. I turn again into a swirling eddy. Now he's running ahead. He's over the flat of the river. I see his legs straddling the water. I try to keep my eyes on his gray head, large and shining in the sun. His arms are open. He is motionless like one of his statues. The river is suddenly shallow and shoots me forward, stretched out, my hands and hair flying out behind me, my feet pointing toward the bridge of Salvador.

He lunges forward from the waist. I fly up into his arms. Stumbling and toppling, he carries me to the grass and sets me down. I don't know if I cry. My mind is full of him waiting to fish me. I only see his large sure head, his gray hair shining with pieces of sun, his wide brown face solemn. Panting, he bends over me on the grass.

I am safe. When my mother comes running up, he has to comfort her. The words they have are for each other. They take me back up the hill to the cloth of the picnic. They wrap me and sit me. Maybe they feed me or scold. They comfort each other. They don't look at me. What he did, he did it for her. What she feels for me, that I did not drown on the day of the picnic, she feels for him who saved me. They are one, and I am not.

Even if they don't see me, the blue above me is mine, below me is a hot white river, which is mine. The race when he carried me in his arms is mine, and the moment he leaned over me, on all fours, panting, is mine.

*

When Mama goes to the hospital, I go with Pilar. The white porcelain bowl under the bed is filled with pieces of blood. Pilar waits for Daddy to call again. He is rushing back from New York. He takes Primo and me with him to bring Mama home, away from her high white bed. Daddy holds her hand against his chest, balancing her on the way to the taxi. She lies in back with her head in his lap. In the front seat, Primo and I have to sit next to each other which we hate.

Mama whispers to me, "Choli, you were almost born in a taxi."

"This one?"

"No, silly. Your father kept saying 'Faster! Faster! The baby's coming!' And the driver yelled, 'Not in my taxi! Not in my taxi!'"

*

At home, Mama lies all day on the sofa. Daddy kneels near her and holds her hand. Mama sobs and they talk softly to each other.

The baby, Leo, the baby.

My poor Darling. And the poor little halfling. Too little. Couldn't.... I'm so sorry I was gone.

Leo, I'm sorry, I was so lonely. I needed you. I needed... everything. But you were rescuing some dreadful woman. I gave up. It's my fault.

No, darling, mine.

I shouldn't have.

I was gone too long.

I thought you were never coming home.

I didn't know if you would take me back. Did you love the man?

Oh, yes. I love him.

Can we fix our lives?

I don't know. I'm so tired.

Can we try?

Maybe we can.

Please, let's try. I would have raised the baby as my own, you know.

I know.

Poor little thing. So, so small.

*

Big Salvador packs the car and goes away with little Chava and the portrait woman—the house emptied in one night. No one knows where they went. I want him to come back.

Mama has a key to Salvador's studio. After they have driven away forever from their house across the street, Mama takes me to his workroom a few blocks away on Higuera Street. We pass the red house of La Malinche. The house of treaties, dialects, agreements, women and betrayals. As we pass the open door, my body almost falls into the cool patio, as if that is where I lived, where I was needed and not needed, seen and not seen, where they used the name Malinche for her and sometimes even for Cortés.

Mama and I enter the studio. Her jade robe is on a hook near the door. A white curtain is pulled open between the clay women he is forming and the plaster statue ready to be cast. I have seen his hand on Mama's hip—Mama disguised, inside a larger woman, with round eyes, larger breasts and giant hands.

Her white marble self had been in the middle of the room. Now there are just pieces.

In my mind, I see him, alone, waiting for word from the hospital. Was his baby killing her, or would it, half-made, tear itself away and spare her? I see him, her Maillol, bellowing, crying over the white skin he had carved from the sight of her thighs. I see the mallet coming down, taking toes, elbows, flattening her stomach, smashing ribs. The hammer slashes at the swoop of her spine—his feet set firm to break, undo, reduce. His gray hair filled with white dust. Dust powdering the sweater that comforted me. My eyes stare at the pieces and I hear him groan, then roar, knowing the exact moment when his baby went to God. My own chest hurts as if it remembers how a piece of his heart tore out in a clot, how a slice of his chest broke and rose like a cradle to lift the small wild ribs of his unborn lamb to heaven.

I see him, cuts on his arms, blood on his face, falling over what is left of her, kissing her white Carrara palm.

Mama is crying. She sees the blood on the marble fingers. She sees in her mind what I see in mine. She pulls giant drawings off the table and rolls them up with rubber bands and we go to the car. There are things she burns in our fireplace at home. I know she will feed these papers to the fire.

Melanie Hoffert
The Allure of Grain Trucks

*D**o you think it's weird that I want to drive a grain truck for a while?" my friend Monica asks me over the phone.*

"A grain truck? Seriously?" I tap my keyboard as I talk and notice that it is filthy, embarrassing almost. The keys are sticky and filled with crumbs. The entire board is splattered with coffee drips. *Disgusting*, I think. Five years of pecking out emails while I hold a sandwich—not wanting to lose time to eat lunch—has started to show.

I visualize Monica, who is working in San Francisco. I see her in a loft with high ceilings and little geometrical work stations lined with Macs. I imagine people wearing dark-rimmed eyeglasses, suit-coats, torn jeans, and sneakers, popping their head into her office and flashing a white smile against tanned skin. Monica herself is covered with tattoos and wears only eighties vintage clothing, an appearance probably more reflective of her passion for music and pop-culture than her day job at a publishing house.

In contrast my office is in a closed, dark corner of a building in Minneapolis. My walls are neutral. My plants are dying. My view is a parking lot. "Your very *own* office? Our baby girl is so important!" my mom would say, looking around at the same space, not noticing the depressing vanilla walls, the crusty plants, or my parking lot view— thrilled by the fact that her *baby girl* has somehow managed to find herself an executive position with all of the perks.

"Yes. Seriously," Monica continues, "I was thinking I could come home—maybe just for a few months—and drive truck through harvest. I could live in that old farm house on my parents' land and

'The Allure of Grain Trucks' previously appeared in the May 2009 issue of Muse & Stone.

'This piece is the first chapter from my book in progress, The Silent Land: A Memoir about God, Gays, and Good North Dakotans. The question I hold in my mind as I write is why people who love each other completely often avoid each other's deepest intimacies. Writing has revealed to me both the beauty of silence (the way it holds space in meditation or defines a landscape), as well as the pain (how lifetimes can pass without truth or reconciliation, even as—in my case—entire communities are reshaped.) My story happens to be about being gay, a secret I held close through my early years on the prairie, then working at a Bible camp, and later as an adult longing for the people I never told. I now know, however, that my issue is not about being gay at all. In fact, I've learned that we all carry our silences and fears. And the most damaging silences are not those of others, but those we carry within.'

~ Melanie Hoffert

then figure out what to do afterwards." She pauses. "You know... I think I'm just ready to get out. I'm ready to leave the city. Plus—seriously—how hard would it be to learn how to drive truck again? I drove when I was fourteen! I mean—I can certainly figure out how to drive now."

"Oh my God. You'd be fine." I give her the old 'you'd be fine' hand wave, as if she can see me. "Pick it back up in no time," I say.

Monica and I are both children of the North Dakota prairie. She grew up in a tiny town near the northern border of the state. I grew up on a farm near a tiny town at about the same longitude on the southern border. These small towns are near identical. They have a railroad that runs through the center, a grain elevator, a gas station, a Catholic church on one side of town, a Lutheran church on the other, and a few bars in between. In fact, our hometowns fit the description of most North Dakota towns.

"I can see you driving a grain truck," I continue, savoring the vision of my thirty-something-San Francisco-tattooed-DJ-friend with dyed black hair driving a grain truck down the gravel roads. Then I imagine all of us—those who left North Dakota—coming back, settling in with the farmers, filling the small town bars at night, Schmidt beer in hand, talking about literature and the grain markets.

"You can?" Monica asks.

"Yes. In fact, maybe we should buy a little farm together; drive truck for some cash." I grab a tissue and start working on a coffee blot on my keyboard while I consider our long term options. "Yeah. Maybe you could start a band and play in the bars at night. I mean, what else is going on there? Um... *nothing*. You'd probably be a hit! Then, after harvest, we could take a road trip. Tour North Dakota. I'll be your crew." I pause, not quite sure if *crew* is the word I'm looking for. I am not into the music scene and feel immediately not so hip. "Or—I'll do something. Carry your guitar? Play the drums? I don't know."

"Would you? Really? You'd come to North Dakota to be my *roadie*?" she laughs.

"Yes! I will. Why not!"

I think of my parents' farm during harvest right then, how harvest nights in the middle of the country seem almost cosmopolitan: bright, moving, awake, and alive. The moon glows like an orange pumpkin in the sky. Trucks light up the yard as they come in from the fields to empty their bounty. Once drained, they return to the dark night for another hit of golden crop from the combines. All of this activity stirs the crisp, corn-filled air, which makes it smell like someone is baking sweet muffins from somewhere deep within the earth. All the while, real cooking is happening inside, where Mom is making hamburgers and fried onions for my dad and brother who will come in exhausted and dirty well past ten o'clock.

"You know, Mo, I think you should make the move." I turn my keyboard upside down and watch the crumbs fall out like dirty snow. "I think *we* should."

Monica and I both left North Dakota after college and moved to the city where we hoped to find something that existed beyond the prairie. At the time, this *something* was unspeakable—our shared secret. But now that we are in our thirties, it just might be time to return home—at least for a sabbatical of some sort—and confront the reasons we left.

"Yes! I think it is time to change our lives!" Monica cheers in her calm and ecstatic way—like a happy, tattooed monk.

"I know. I could really use a break from work. From life. From the traffic and the busyness. I mean, how long can we go on like this!" I am being dramatic now, resorting to our college chatter. It is easy to fall into this lingo with Monica. In college we spent long nights together in her small, carpeted apartment talking about our lives. She played her electric guitar without an amp. I sat across from her on her Salvation Army couch, chewing sunflower seeds and spitting them into a blue mug. The next morning we did the same. She sat in her ripped pajamas, picking at her electric guitar, and I drank coffee from the same blue mug. I often crashed for the night at her place, too tired to drive across town to my own bed in a small house I shared with three other women. I am about to remind her of this, of our time together, when someone pops a frenzied head in my office.

"Hey, ah, you got a minute?"

I keep my eyes on the intruder and switch to my I-am-at-work-and-trying-to-be-professional-voice, which I can barely pull out for Monica. "Excuse me, Monica. Can I interrupt you for just one minute? Yes. Sorry. Let's talk soon and *seriously* consider our... our...." I look at the person standing in my door, "our future *business proposition*."

She gets my drift. "Oh sure. Yes. Call me later."

After I deal with the person who wants to know if I can set up a meeting to discuss something we had just discussed, I look out of my window. I notice the landscape: the parking lot, the cement, the buildings, the way my eye is stopped by a delivery truck blocking my view of the earth.

*

I am lucky, aren't I? Let's add it up. One: In my early thirties and success- ful for my age, with a team of thirty and budget of millions. Two: A home in the city with access to restaurants and film. Three…. Three… *What is THREE?*

I am happy, right? Why, then, does the thought of listening to AM radio and pulling my truck up to a grain elevator in a small North Dakota town have my heart fluttering with excitement? Why does the vision of sitting in a little North Dakota bar hitting a tambourine against my thigh, while Monica sings to a crowd of men in John Deere hats and women in over-sized sweatshirts, make me ache with purpose?

I throw my tissue away, take a breath, accept my dirty keyboard, and go back to work. Both Monica and I know that our daydream of another life—in this case, returning to a past life—will probably only carry us through the next hour. Returning home would be impossible. Or would it?

*

Over the last ten years I have been trying to resolve a seemingly simple dilemma: How to tell the state of North Dakota that I am gay. This might sound crazy, but if you are from the heart of the country you might understand that you are part of a world that is more connected than any social networking phenomenon of the digital age. Your personal profile is peeked at, commented on, and updated at every home-town shower, funeral, wedding, pig roast, street dance, and Sunday morning church service—even if you don't live in the small town anymore. If you have a secret, it does not necessarily belong to you, or your family, or even God. It belongs to the place you are from, because eventually to resolve everything, to truly find peace, you must come to terms with the place your inner-soul calls home.

In my case, this place is the North Dakota prairie.

The longer I drag my feet on this issue—my confession—the fewer people there are left in North Dakota to tell. At last count, North Dakota—well, the middle of the country for that matter—has been emptying faster than the draining of a butchered cow. A recent National Geographic issue ran an article called "The Emptied Prairie," which featured my home state and its painfully irreversible population decline. The pictures in the article showed abandoned farmhouses in hauntingly dilapidated conditions, barren except for a few signs of life: a dusty doll, a wedding veil hanging in a bare room, an old woman looking forlorn out of a window onto the empty prairie. The pictures reminded me of villages left behind after military raids: One minute there is life and normalcy, the next stillness and emptiness.

Some attribute this loss to economics or lack of opportunity for young people. I think this emptying—at a cellular or even metaphysical level—has something to do with an even deeper issue: prairie silence. At least my emptying did.

*

My life resembles something that good North Dakotans might describe as a "spinster's" life. I am a tad past thirty, very independent, the oldest in my family, not married (of course), and I live with two cats. I refuse to get three for fear that I might graduate from spinster lady to cat lady, a far worse label.

"You met a fella yet?" The North Dakotans started asking almost ten years ago, every time I returned home to visit my family. I think they assumed I had ventured into the world to find what used to be down the gravel road, working in the neighbor's barn: a good man.

"Ah. No. Nope. No." I'd respond in a nervous babble, trying to act normal even while my breathing changed to panic-attack shallow and I started screaming at the innocent questioner in my mind. Good Lord, do NOT go there. Please. Please talk about your crops or the latest funeral or the church turkey supper. Anything else but the fella! There was simply no way for me to tell them the truth.

And because they assumed comforting words were in order, they offered the following. "Well. This day and age? People are getting married later and later. Pretty gal like you? You'll find someone. A good one. You won't be alone for long!"

I have never been as alone as it may appear to the North Dakotans. When I first moved to the city meeting people was like watching Mom unpack ornaments for our Christmas tree. She would sink her hands deep into the plastic tub and slowly pull small figures out of crinkly tissue paper, retrieving wiry stars, handmade decorated ginger bread cookies sprayed and preserved, colorful little quilted balls, and baby Jesuses with chipped cheeks. Each ornament had its own color, texture, history, and story. Similarly, in the city I met people making art, people wearing art, people with pet pigs; I witnessed lives being pulled together, lives being torn apart. I experienced, for the first time, a taste of diversity outside of the world of farmers.

I also had a very active night life, exploring the world of the gays, as we might be called on the prairie. On Saturday nights beautiful and mysterious women sauntered into bars. I watched the parade completely captivated: there were the hipsters, the academics, the granolas, and the tomboys. They were all shapes, sizes, and colors with one common trait: confidence. Where do they all come from, I wondered? Not from North Dakota, I thought.

Before moving to Minneapolis I had experienced only the Fargo Bowler, where once a month they held an underground gay dance. On those nights I scanned the crowds of flannel-clad older women, skinny gay men and young college ravers—who were not gay, but claimed the space as an alternative stomping ground—to find someone a bit younger, a bit more like me. I had a vision, I think, of someone who looked like my childhood best friend; someone with an athletic body, feminine disposition, with a strong will, bright eyes, and dark hair. I, myself, would have probably fit in better at the sorority parties, with my lipstick, my eyeliner. I had been groomed to be this—feminine, colorful, a perfect contrast for my prom dates in their black and white tuxes. I watched the women at these dances drink beer and scan the crowds. Ironically, the scene reminded me of a table filled with men at a small town cafe. I did not yet understand the subtleties of gender politics or butch fem dynamics or how later similar women would take me under their wing. At the time I simply wasn't interested in dating older women who still reminded me of a fella.

That was all over ten years ago. I now prefer evenings with a bath and a book to those out on the town. I have settled into a relationship with a woman I consider my partner. She is raising a daughter, so on evenings when her ex has her child we drink red wine, talk about life, linger in our yards or pick at our gardens. Often we make slow meals with fresh herbs, sizzling garlic, and sweet onions, mixing ingredients until the house bleeds with the delicious and complex aroma of a gourmet meal. On these nights I am not alone. I am not a spinster. Yet, this would be news back home.

*

Last year when my sister announced her wedding engagement, I requested that she substitute my Maid of Honor title with a new title of my own creation: The Best Sister. I knew I would be encountering everyone from my past at her wedding—those who have known me since I was in diapers, but who had never once asked me if I am gay. The Best Sister title was a tiny act of public rebellion on my part, as if to tell the North Dakotans that I don't believe in titles, and I will not be understood or defined by my marital status!

As we lined up to enter the church on her wedding day, sweat poured down my chest. I wasn't worried about my shoes, my dress, crying, or how my sister looked—which I think was supposed to be part of my job. Instead I was worried only about the programs, those two hundred little pieces of paper floating in the audience, now converted to fans and rolled up into little tubes, stuffed into pockets and shoved into hymnals. They know! They finally know! Then— What, actually, do they know? I asked myself, sarcastically. A response came from nowhere. That I'm different! And right then I felt liberated. My step became confident. I held my flowers tightly and proudly marched toward the altar as if I was finally going to marry my truth.

As my sister exchanged vows I decided to tune out the whole thing about women being derived from man's rib, which made me visualize human ribs coated in barbecue sauce. Instead, I practiced how I would respond when my old neighbors and teachers and pastors and high school friends made a wise crack about my Best Sister title. Yes, I decided to become a Best Sister because I will not be defined by my relationship status, I'd tell them. And while they would stand there—confused—because what I've said doesn't make a lick of sense, I would tap my chin, as if just hit with the most random thought, say, along the lines… *for about twenty years—well, my whole life really—I have been meaning to tell you that I prefer to date women.*

Good North Dakotans, if you must know, would usually make a smart comment. Best Sister, eh? What, 'cha get a medal or something? Win some sort of award in the big city? Then they'd grab me around the shoulder, clunk my drink with their plastic beer glass, squeeze me, and say, Cheers. As if to say, Just teasing kiddo. They'd make a comment, that is, unless they didn't want to hear a response.

That night when the band started to play and the dance unfolded as most small town wedding dances will, I waited and watched. Old people sat around the parameter of the dance floor on folding chairs, drinking coffee and visiting. Little kids chased each other, screaming like baby hyenas. Women kicked off their shoes. Men loosened their ties. People pulled me out to dance and bounced me around like a tether ball. The night unfolded as planned, but nobody brought up the Best Sister. Realizing nobody was going to confront me, I took big gulps of my gin and tonic and relaxed. My shoulders fell, my chest became light; I slid across the dance floor and looped arms with family and people I've known since childhood. I welcomed, once again, the familiar and numbing comfort of our silence.

*

Two years ago Monica got a tattoo of North Dakota on her wrist. The tattoo is an outline of the state with a tiny star marking the location of Northwood, her hometown. Next she got a tattoo of the word *Heartland* down the middle of her arm. In ways the tattoos symbolize how far she's clearly grown from her farming roots as well as how deeply rooted she really is.

"What do you think I should tell my parents?" she asked me after her first tattoo, a star on her shoulder. In truth, I had no idea how to respond. All I could think about was Monica's mom, a Lutheran church organist for over twenty years, who put Monica into finishing school in college. At this school Monica had to learn to walk down the stairs sideways and balance books on her head. "She's teaching me how to be a fancy *lady*, so I know how to be with *sophisticated* people," Monica would complain, though she did as she was told. How *would* her mom react to the tattoos, after investing so much in a vision of her daughter, a vision she hoped would help Monica grow beyond the small town and make something of herself in the larger world? I couldn't fathom.

*

Monica and I became friends in college during one of the worst winters in North Dakota history. It was in 1997, the year when melting snowdrifts—some crashing like waves over houses and cars—created record spring flooding in the Red River Valley. Fargo city officials ordered residents to stay inside, out of the eighty-degree-below wind-chill. Anyone who disobeyed, they threatened on TV, would receive a ticket.

Knowing we would be locked in our house for days when the blizzards hit, my three roommates and I scurried to the grocery store in our parkas and our flannel pajamas to stock up on food and supplies. Monica, at first a friend of one of my roommates, drove from her tiny apartment on the other side of town, not wanting to be alone during the storm. While big flakes fell from the sky we took naps, cooked frozen pizzas, made pancakes, and flipped to the weather station to get updates between movies. The little house was barely big enough for one person, let alone five. But this was college, when a house filled with friends was more important than a house filled with space and nice furniture. We ignored time over those long days, which I now realize is a rare gift of a contented mind.

Monica was a quiet girl who wanted to be a musician and worked at the Fargo Theater, the only place in the state of North Dakota where you could catch independent films. She wore faded jeans, button-up shirts over band T-shirts, and pulled her hair up on each side of her head, clipping it with a single barrette.

On one of the blizzard nights when my roommates went to bed early, Monica changed the course of our relationship. The house was quiet. Monica and I were playing cards under the glow of red Christmas lights. She tossed me the question as freely as she tossed me a King of Spades.

"Are you a Heartbreaker?"

As soon as the words left her lips my palms began to sweat. At that time not even my roommates knew I was gay. We attended a private Lutheran College and they were all very good church girls who had not yet kissed a boy. I, on the other hand, had gone to prom, dated boys, and had plenty of back seat rendezvous. I was the experienced one, so my lack of boy fever was never considered all too odd.

"That's a strange question. What do you *mean*?" I said grabbing her king, pretending to all of a sudden be consumed with our game.

"Why is it *strange*? Because you are one?" Her voice was serious.

"Are one—what?"

"A Heartbreaker! Are you a Heartbreaker!" I sat up straight in my chair. The quiet girl who barely said a word when she was at our house asked this with such intensity and directness it was as if another person had just entered the room and stepped into her body. I wasn't sure where to go with her question. Besides it being rather odd, it was also as if she was accusing me of something.

"I... wouldn't... say... so, exactly," I responded cautiously. She just stared at me. "I mean, no. No! I am not a Heartbreaker. Why are you asking?"

"Really? What would *Samantha* say?" A cold wind seemed to

shake the house. Samantha was the first woman I dated at college. My relationship with her was the antithesis of what I had imagined a relationship with a woman would be. Our relationship had ended two years earlier. I certainly hadn't broken her heart. In fact, I thought she had crushed mine.

Where might this be going? I wondered. I could understand Monica fishing for a confession of my secret life, one which I had shared with only a handful of new friends. But Monica's accusations seemed to be less about my being gay than being a Heartbreaker. I didn't understand.

"Frankly, I don't care what Samantha says." Another card. "So, you obviously must know her?"

"Yes. She knows my roommate, Laura."

"Oh. So, you must know a lot about me then," I said, my heart pounding now. I was unpracticed, still frozen when it came to talking about my desire to be in a relationship with a woman. I tried to act calm, as if I had been through this discussion a hundred times. "Did Samantha say I am a Heartbreaker or something?"

Monica didn't respond. Instead she got up and went to the couch where she sat, pulled her knees close to her chest, and rocked back and forth. Her face turned white. I followed her. I was confused, scared, and curious. I was the one who was now exposed. I was the one with the secret! Why was she shaking like a small hurt animal?

"Are you okay?" I asked.

Then they came.

Words flowed from her body like lava that had been waiting a thousand years to touch the air. She was shaking, spilling stories of a long-time love affair with her female basketball coach from high school. The woman, now a coach at a neighboring college, had ended their several-year-long relationship to date another girl.

Monica's interrogation was not about me, it was about her. Her angry accusation quickly fizzled as her more authentic need emerged: the need to share her story before she bled to death internally. Like me, she kept her feelings a secret, one she did not share with another living soul—not her family, not her friends, not her small town. Her fear forced her to deal with the most dramatic and painful experience of her life—the death of a first love—in complete silence. I had done the same, years earlier. Monica had decided that the demise of her pure love could only be explained by thinking of her ex-love as someone she didn't really know, someone capable of being a Heartbreaker.

On that blizzard night we talked until dawn, putting words to years of silence, like finally putting words to music. And over the next year, our senior year, Monica became my closest friend. She ventured with me to the Fargo Bowler where we danced into the night with women and men who came from nowhere and disappeared into that nowhere when the night ended. Convinced we were the only lesbians in the world under sixty, we promised each other that we would move after graduation.

Monica moved to San Francisco, dyed her hair, learned how to DJ, started a band, and joined the hipster counter-culture queers in the Mission. Her San Francisco friends are not *from* San Francisco. They have all drifted there, restless souls like Monica, looking to the city to free them, fulfill them, inspire and deliver them to a paradise of like-minded people.

I moved to Minneapolis, focused on my career, bought a house, started graduate school and befriended women who spent more in one evening on dinner than the free spirits in Monica's San Francisco made in one week. Monica and I took different paths, but are still connected by our beginning, a beginning we both still crave.

*

In a recent North Dakota election there was a measure on the ballot proposing that anyone under thirty who lived and worked in the state would receive a thousand dollars a year to pay off their student loan debt. The measure failed.

Some living in the state are trying to put a tourniquet on the gaping wound through which many educated and ambitious young people leave. The state is desperate for revival. And even though the *National Geographic* article generated letters from the angry North Dakotans wanting to defend the viability and fruitfulness of the state, I doubt the most optimistic North Dakotan could ever imagine a restoration of rural America, of towns with populations ranging from 30 to 2,000. The small town, it seems, is dying into extinction.

Over the years I have learned that the one personal disclaimer that will cause pause—when I am on a business trip to New York for example—is not about dating women. The eyebrow raiser is this:

"I'm originally from North Dakota."

"North Dakota?"

My new acquaintances always repeat my statement in the form of a question, as if I must have been mistaken.

"North Dakota," I say with a shrug.

"Wow!" They tilt their heads. "*Really?*"

"Yes. Really."

At this point they'll get a smug grin. "Now, tell me. What in the world is North Dakota like?" as if I am about to deliver the punch line.

This is a difficult question for me. Somehow, I want to explain to them that the land is beautiful, beyond their imagination. But I am stopped, like when I bring my city friends back to the farm. When the houses thin and we are eventually surrounded by nothingness I suddenly lose my vision. The world looks bleak, flat, unpromising and colorless. I start apologizing as if I had dragged them to an empty art gallery.

"The view is… kind of the ugly time of year," I'll say.

Yet when I return to the farm on my own, and am not responsible for another person's eyes, the land speaks to me in another way. Rediscovering the landscape of North Dakota is like finding a familiar childhood book with soft pages that smell sweet with age. The flat land is not dry, not dark, not lifeless. Instead North Dakota is a painter's palette where all of the earthly colors settle. The light changes minute by minute, following unassuming subjects: a wheat field, a gravel road, a gray grain elevator. When I squint I can almost see the bottom of glacial Lake Agassiz, the ancient lake that left the Red River Valley fertile and flat. The rows in the fields are the sand ripples of the lake bottom. The shelterbelts are large alien sea plants, reaching to the light. The sky is the surface of the lake reflecting the sun.

"North Dakota is actually very beautiful," is all I will say to my new acquaintances. They'll look at me with a suspicious eye, as if to say, *What could emptiness possibly hold?*

*

Over the years, I came home to find that not only had businesses closed, but they were actually gone. Completely vanished. Today, my home town's main street resembles the mouth of an old woman who is missing most of her teeth. A few brick buildings still stand, surrounded by spaces that will never be filled.

I cannot say why, exactly, it matters that these buildings are gone. Though I think it has something to do with driving through any part of the country and being solicited by the same chain stores with the same brands with the same colors and the same goods, whether you are in Arizona or Minnesota. The only difference in some of these places is the natural world, the lakes and the cacti, reminding us of contrast, of hot and cold, of mountains and valleys. I frequent the assimilated superstores; they have trained me to know their aisles, to be thankful that in a hurried stop that I can retrieve Glad trash bags or Tide by walking straight for four aisles and turning left, whether I am in Utah or Ohio.

Or maybe it matters that these businesses are gone because of the people, something to do with visions of my parents' friends, business owners and farmers, who took jobs in larger towns pushing papers and drinking coffee out of Styrofoam cups, making small talk with co-workers and answering to a boss in a stale, florescent-lit office.

As I ponder those of us who have left the prairie, I wonder what stories we take with us and what longer stories we end. There are, of course, those few kids who don't end up leaving the prairie. They are the ones who take over family businesses or marry their high school sweethearts. These people become the material of the next generation, the thin fabric that keeps the community connected and viable. Of those who do leave, I think there are two manifestations of the departed.

First, there are the few who leave early and permanently. They escape into the larger world and truly disappear. Their face is forever frozen on the walls of the high school in their senior picture.

Then there are the rest of us. The in-betweens. We leave, but we never truly leave. Our families are connected to the community like trees to the earth. We are bound to this place we still call home, to people we call neighbors and friends. But some of us must keep the familiar at arms length because of prairie silence.

Prairie silence is—I have come to believe—the way the people of the prairie mirror the land with their sturdy, hard working, fruitful, and quiet dispositions. They are committed to each other like the soil is committed to the crop. They are uncomplaining in the way the land dutifully recovers after blizzards, droughts and floods. They are humble and quiet, like white prairie grass in the wind. They swallow their problems, their fears, their shames, and their secrets—figuring that nature will take care of everything, somehow or other. That is, after all, how it works with the crops. And once a silence has taken hold, whatever it is, it is hard to uproot.

*

I haven't always been fond of the farm. As a child I made a stink about living in the middle of nowhere. I made sure Mom knew how unfair it was that the town kids had to ride their bikes only a few blocks to see friends. I had to ride mine at least three miles.

"Honey, believe me, you wouldn't like to live in town. All those people..." my mom would say. She was the authority, the only one in my family who had ever lived in a town, having grown up in Wahpeton, North Dakota. "Plus, you can play with the Holtzes anytime you like."

The Holtz kids lived three miles down the gravel road, a good bike ride away, and could have very well lived in the trees. They were stocky and strong, three boys and a girl, with deep-gravely laughs, freckles, dark hair, and eyes lit with a sort of devious wild joy. At their farm my brother and I spent hours riding in creaky wagons connected to lawn mowers, engines the Holtzes had turned into small vehicles. The Holtzes were like pirates on the sea, piled up on their small tractor, headbands and dirty faces, looking into the horizon, and pulling us down well worn paths they carved into the shelter belts by their farm.

The Holtz kids were earth kids. They belonged in the trees. In another time and place, they would have settled on the land—I am quite sure—connected by a deep and long tradition, by a pulse running through their blood. Yet their parents had to move off of the farm before their oldest child was old enough to go to high school. My brother and I were devastated to lose our dirty-faced friends, the only friends we could visit without having to get into a car. Today all of the Holtz kids live in towns far away from their small farm, far from the abandoned paths they carved into the trees such a long time ago.

*

Sometimes I wonder if I will be the last generation of my family to live on the land, to know the land. Or sometimes I wonder if am the first generation of a larger kind: The first generation of people to leave the land, the small towns, the Lutheran churches, where they still make coffee by cracking eggs into the grounds, behind. The first generation to realize that the world of rural America—both the good and the bad of it—will never again be as it once was. The first generation to look back and say, with sadness, *I cannot return.*

Is silence, *my* silence, this powerful? Maybe.

Lucy Sieger
Domestic Insurgency

*S*ome women in troubled marriages fake orgasms. I faked a cake.

It wasn't like I never faked an orgasm, although my first husband and I had devolved to a "don't ask / don't tell" policy. But my faking of a homemade cake had common ground with that more intimate deception: fatigue (let's get this over with), exasperation (he won't know the difference), impatience (that Carol Shields novel on the nightstand). Mostly, my cake-faking was the manifestation of a forbidden whisper that uncoiled in my brain, like wisps of mutinous smoke: *You don't have to be his wife anymore.*

My bond with John was our shared assumption that I was lucky to have him. He was charismatic, charming, a successful sales manager for an international corporation. Freed from the shackles of a full-time job, I went to graduate school and accompanied him to conventions in venues like Palm Springs and Maui. After I scratched my academic itch, I was to buckle down and have a baby. Like the well-groomed women in his large affluent family, I would climb into the harness of proper wife and mother. Meanwhile, I should ignore the incessant hang-up phone calls and occasional lies about his whereabouts.

Sometimes I would scrutinize John's handsome face, searching for some faint flicker I could connect to. But those sparkly blue eyes, snappy and persuasive in the business world, grew opaque at home. I knew I was defective. Yet he tolerated my unworthiness, even showed me collegial affection at times, so I burrowed into the considerable comforts of my gilded cage. Everyone compromised in this world, right? Nothing was ideal. I grew accustomed to a muffled life, as if I were underwater.

'I write personal essays about ordinary, even mundane experiences. But my hope is to spin a unique perspective, one that relates a particular episode to universal emotions, and invites the reader to consider those emotions in fresh ways.'

~ Lucy Sieger

Eventually, I finished graduate school. Instead of going off birth control, as John suggested, I accepted a position as writer and editor for an academic institute. From that very first day, I discovered I had charisma too, albeit a quieter sort. My new colleagues liked me. I was funny, they told me, I was an excellent writer. Some older ladies in the office said I looked like a model. At five feet ten inches, this was mostly due to my statuesque height. But still, the compliments bolstered my shriveled self-esteem, and my clothes shrank as my confidence grew. After years of swaddling myself in baggy jeans and dowdy turtlenecks, I began wearing skirts, form-fitting slacks, and sweaters that actually exposed my collarbones.

One lunch hour, I attended a seminar about the company's new computer system. The consultant was from England, tall, with an impish grin and snazzy continental suits. His accent was more chimney sweep than aristocrat, but it was British, and dozens of women predictably and collectively swooned. As he began his presentation, he scanned the packed room, and our eyes locked. He stared at me, speechless for a long moment, until the concerned murmurs of the audience jolted him back to his PowerPoint slides. He thinks I'm pretty, I realized, stunned and blushing. He thinks I'm pretty. I never exchanged more than pleasantries with him, but our thirty-second love affair transformed me.

I grew pensive at home. My vague marriage seemed inappropriate to this new, fledgling me, and I didn't know how to work the revised equation. Meanwhile, sensing a shift, John's desire for a child grew more strident. I waffled. I loved writing and editing, and I wanted to be a working mother—if I had a child at all, I told him. That was the first time John threatened to divorce me.

His birthday was soon after, the week before Christmas, and he insisted on a cake made from scratch. My brow furrowed into a ridge of frustration. Hadn't I spent days shopping and shipping gifts to his huge family? Hadn't I cooked and cleaned for a dinner party of eight last weekend? Hadn't I written out dozens of holiday cards? What had he done, outside of stringing a few lights on the tree? I was exhausted, but I also knew he wanted proof of an obsequience I no longer felt. My fuming quickly turned to scheming.

The night before his birthday, while he was at the gym, I turned up the blistering rebellion of Alanis Morrissette on the stereo. I propped open *The Joy of Cooking* to page 287 and displayed the recipe for vanilla white cake, front and center on my cookbook stand. Then, with a smirk, I excavated the box of cake mix and can of frosting from the murky depths of our pantry. I cackled like a witch stirring her cauldron, dropping bat claws and worm lips into the brew, flavoring the dusty powdered mix with my deceitful naughtiness.

The cake must have absorbed my exhilaration, because it was amazingly good. "I really appreciate the trouble you went to," John said, smiling at me after he devoured his slice. He even held my hand.

"Happy birthday, sweetie," I replied. Any twinge of guilt was muted, an artifact of my former self.

One evening right after Christmas, walking down the driveway to get the mail, John noticed a scrap of paper on the ground, near the curb, where we put the trash cans on pick-up day. It was a grocery receipt. He picked it up and read it, the flimsy glow of the streetlamp illuminating my pixilated epitaph:

Betty Crocker vanilla cake mix...$2.24
Pillsbury chocolate frosting...$1.23

Later, we would divorce, and I would stumble into an intense love affair that left me raw and alive. I would long for a child with this man I adored, and I would weep primal, hormonal tears when I was too old. But we would have a life together, and a home. I would whisk together vinaigrettes of Dijon mustard and champagne vinegar. I would melt musky chocolate chips into bubbling cream and drizzle the glacé over homemade brownies. I would bake aromatic crostatas of apples and cinnamon and brown sugar, my domesticity as boundless as this different, truer love.

John would marry a younger woman, beautiful, friends said. She would have his child; she would be his corporate dream wife. We had our happy ending, just not together.

But for that moment, confronted by John in our oval dining room, both of us dwarfed by the high, domed ceiling, I wavered on the jagged precipice between before and after. In the dim light of a fading marriage, I saw the sad, deflated man before me with the frightening clarity of one newly emerged. His thin veil of confidence was pierced, our relationship more tattered than the grocery receipt he clutched in his trembling hand, both of us lost as to what to do next.

John Updike at Rest...

The Late Great Author on Writing About Sex, God...
And A Rabbit Who Worried Himself to Death

By Don Williams

Of all the celebrity deaths of 2009, the toughest for NMW surely was that of John Updike, who died of lung cancer on Jan. 27, 2009. This genial man of flamboyant letters brought instant credibility to New Millennium Writings in 1996, when he agreed to be interviewed for our start-up literary journal. Here is that first-ever NMW interview/profile, anachronisms and all.—DW

While researching *Rabbit at Rest*, John Updike made the long drive south to Florida that Harry "Rabbit" Angstrom, his unruly protagonist in four novels would make just weeks before his fictive death.

"I drove a little farther than Harry. I drove down from Boston, through the Brewer Diamond County area in Pennsylvania, then south," says Updike. "There isn't an awful lot to see on Route 95. You're in a tunnel of green. I watched the rivers I crossed and listened to the radio." Recasting the journey in fiction, Updike used it to bring Rabbit closer to death and to set him reflecting upon the passages of his life as they were evoked by music on the radio.

Think of Updike's career as a literary ride through four decades of American life and you get a sense of what may be his greatest achievement. He has chronicled, at times almost catalogued, the hopes, fears, sexual trends and pop artifacts of our times more vividly than any other writer.

His novel, *In the Beauty of the Lilies*, (Knopf, 1996) extended Updike's reach to embrace a century. The book begins with a Presbyterian minister waking up to the icy conviction that there is no God. He spends the next 100 pages avoiding hypocrisy by giving up his church,

'When you come to the practice of your art you have to go with what thrills you. If you wrote some opposite way, you would get criticized for that. You have to please yourself.'

~ John Updike

his home and social standing. His children and grandchildren fare both better and worse as the years march past. The book ends on an apocalyptic note reminiscent of the Waco inferno.

Updike has rendered a portrait of America busy losing its faith while embracing pop culture, especially the movies. The cast of characters is broad and vivid, ranging from the proud minister to a movie queen; from a fanatical Bible-quoting guru to a greenhouse attendant, and from Prohibition-era crooks to a warm-hearted mailman.

Rabbit may be the character closest to Updike's heart, however, as if Rabbit were the person Updike might most nearly resemble had he stayed in Shillington, Pennsylvania, where he was born in 1932. Updike's father taught high school math and his mother wrote with modest success. From these beginnings, Updike scaled greater heights than Rabbit ever imagined (and we know the things he imagined). Updike graduated from Harvard in 1954 and won a scholarship to the Ruskin School of Drawing and Fine Art in Oxford, England. From 1955 to 1957 he was a member of the staff of *The New Yorker*, which published his short stories and poems. His first novels were *The Poorhouse Fair* (1959) and *Rabbit, Run* (1960), followed by *The*

Centaur (1963) which won several prizes. Some 45 volumes of verse, essays, stories, novels, plays and autobiography followed. No year went by for more than five decades without his byline appearing. The books have garnered numerous awards, including two Pulitzers and the William Dean Howells Award. Of all this outpouring of prose and verse, the four Rabbit books have earned the greatest fame. Well, those and *The Witches of Eastwick* (1984), which became a popular movie.

Updike once called the *Rabbit* quartet his "continental magnum opus," exploring "the whole mass of middling, hidden, troubled America." Yet Rabbit represents only one corner of the Updike oeuvre. In his novel, *Brazil* (1994), as in *Collected Poems, 1953 to 1993*, you see (or is writing actually *heard*?): A multitude of voices, a flexibility of tone, an extravagance of metaphor, a cosmic range of interests, all kept intelligible through a flowing syntax.

Updike has been accused of? credited with? elevating style above substance. He once described a character's seething anger so: "A flamingo in her voice seeking to flaunt its vivid wings." Thus Updike flaunts his vivid style. But when your major subjects are gratification of the flesh and the search for meaning in a world that people have rendered Godless, and when you plumb such themes in stories about midlife crises, infidelity and death, it's hard to make the charge of stylistic frivolity stick. Updike fishes deep waters.

That may not be immediately apparent to those who show up for a personal appearance, such as the one I attended in Knoxville, Tennessee (ca. 1995—DW).

Dwarfed by the cavernous insides of a rococo movie house where he stood trim in a dark suit, his white hair neatly in place above straight teeth and that famous yam of a nose, Updike read and took questions. His voice is mid-to-low register and spiced by a tone of mild irony, so you have a hard time matching the laid back style of his delivery with THE STYLE in his books.

"I've been accused of being too wordy and colorful since the very beginning of my career, but the writers who excited me were like Proust, who was the master of metaphor," says Updike. "The prolonged metaphors and similes in Proust thrilled me. When you come to the practice of your art you have to go with what thrills you. If you wrote some opposite way, you would get criticized for that. You have to please yourself."

Asked to describe the major theme of his work, Updike demurs, "I'm not sure I'm the one to answer that, but, at a stab... the glory of the daily."

'I think the loss of meaning we were just discussing affects literature above all. Without there being some point to human lives, why bother? What is the point of most of the fiction you read? It seems to have no point.'

Understand, "the daily" can be as chilling as a baby's drowning, as flamboyant as the sexual mores of the New England middle class, or as quirky as Updike's distinct stutter that even now recurs in odd moments. It disappears when he gets rolling, for instance when he's talking about *Brazil*, a magical-realism experiment about a young black beach bum and a wealthy white girl who meet on Copacabana Beach in 1966 and flee westward. The book is at once mystical, violent and sexually charged.

As evidenced by *Memoirs of the Ford Administration* (1993), Updike obviously preferred writing about sex in the Sixties and Seventies rather than the Nineties.

"My period of expertise is pre-AIDS," he says. "The whole thing (AIDS) strikes me as terribly sad and a lot of clutter around what should be a rather pure act. Of course, there was always disease and unwanted pregnancy. That was the bane of sex in the old days. Maybe it's never been as free an activity as it seemed in the 1960s, but the era between the advent of the birth control pill and AIDS was exceptionally innocent and..."

"Fun?" I suggest.

"Yes, fun," he chuckles.

Updike's chronicles of such fun brought him fame. *Rabbit, Run* (1960), the story of a young man's botched flight from his wife and children, and of their eventual reconciliation, was daring in its day. Pages were cut from the manuscript that were not restored to print until later editions.

"John Cheever in some of his letters complains about my 'sexual extravagance.' And I had a terrible time at *The New Yorker*, getting certain expressions in, but I always thought it was healthy to see how far they would go. The late S.J. Perelman thought I wrote about masturbation too much.

"By 1960, when *Rabbit Run* appeared, that taboo business had sort of evaporated. *Lady Chatterly* was coming out and the Henry Miller books. He is not a writer I admire, but I did admire his frankness. He caught something of the real shameless power of the sex drive. The last chapter of Joyce's *Ulysses*, about Molly Bloom, is a model of sexual freedom. Frankness mingles with all kinds of other daily concerns. It's really a very beautiful book. I was influenced by that and (D. H.) Lawrence's courage in trying to write a book about sex, about what happens between men and women.

"And Nabakov's *Lolita*. There's not a dirty word in it, but he did try to show love and sex in what would be considered perverted circumstances. Surely his books are illuminating. Sex is not a simple nor always a healthy thing. It has a twisted side."

Perhaps Updike portrayed that side most vividly in *Couples* (1968).

"*Couples* was written in the full flush of permissible freedom," remembers Updike. "A few complained, mostly to my face or in letters. My attempt was to describe things as they are, with all the attendant embarrassment and awkwardness. It was sexual realism rather than pornography, part of being human. I try to make the books as good as I can and as honest as I can."

Rabbit Run was shocking for reasons other than its sexual candor, however. Two-thirds through the book, there is a long stream-of-consciousness passage in which Updike portrays a young mother, Rabbit's wife Ruth, drowning her baby girl. Reading it is like being tied to a railroad track and watching a train run over you. Few passages in modern fiction strike with such force, a result achieved in part by Updike's switching voices, so that the account is from the mother's point of view.

"In a novel of any length you should be able to enter some other character's mind," says Updike. "In part, the genius of the novel is to demonstrate different points of view. *Rabbit Run* does it more than any other book of mine. I was quite a young novelist at the time I wrote it. I wasn't eager to kill off a character, even a tiny character like Little Becky. It was distasteful, a little like putting a pet down. I was in Vermont with my then-wife, trying to write a little each day. I stayed all day up in my room to write that scene.

"Getting into her head, well, you make a little jump and there you are. It's kind of like jumping into cold water. It's not so bad once you get used it."

'Not to believe in God seems a terrible confession of meaninglessness.... Science isn't very helpful on this, but you also have the datum of your own existence, your own inner being, which, as Kierkegaard and others pointed out, should be taken into account too.'

Updike got used to it quickly. He made similar leaps in novels that followed. In *Rabbit Redux* (1971) the major characters are on drugs, and so Updike made the leap into altered states.

"In the Sixties there was quite of lot of pot around and even though I was a suburban father, householder and all that, the odd chance to smoke pot came along. I don't think I ever got addicted to it, but there was enough around. Coke was not part of my generation's experience, so I'm quite innocent about coke. It's a fine line between what you have to experience and what you can imagine."

Rabbit Redux imagines an America under siege from within. Rabbit's home becomes a commune for his adolescent son Nelson, a runaway teenaged girl named Jill, and a black radical named Skeeter.

"I was trying to show Harry (Rabbit) as a kind of American Everyman being invaded by the most disruptive, scoffing and negative elements of the era. Skeeter was patterned on books more than people I knew. I suppose that Eldridge Cleaver of *Soul on Ice* must have been in there somewhere. It's a little hard to remember, but the Berkeley *Barb* and other dramatically left publications were amply quoted in the press in those days, so that Skeeter's kind of rhetoric was in the air.

"Jill and Skeeter are almost like nightmares Rabbit's having. His little house there on Villa Crescent becomes a kind of clearing house for contemporary thought.

Chronicles of Rabbit's travails and triumphs during the age of excess in *Rabbit Is Rich* (1981) and the era of AIDS and political correctness in *Rabbit at Rest* (1990) earned Updike his Pulitzers. The latter Rabbit books are longer than the first two, but the same techniques and obsessions pertain. Both novels climax, ahem, by way of sexual encounters—a wife-swapping episode in *Rabbit is Rich* and Rabbit's tryst with his daughter-in-law in *Rabbit at Rest*.

At the same time, both are rich with musings about God and time and death, subjects that turn up one way or another in all of Updike's novels, perhaps most notably in a trilogy he based on Hawthorne's *The Scarlet Letter* comprised of *A Month of Sundays* (1975), *Roger's Version* (1986) and *S* (1988).

"I'm very interested in religious issues," says Updike, a church-going Episcopalian.

"Do you believe in God?" I ask.

"Sure. Not to believe in God seems a terrible confession of meaninglessness. *In the Beauty of the Lilies* is an investigation of faith that flickers in and out. I confess I don't think too much about the details, like the Virgin Birth, although there comes a crunch time where you really should make up your mind about those things. The articles of faith were hammered out by thinking men. They're sort of a piece, but I'm not very rigorous, not being a theologian.

"Science isn't very helpful on this," Updike understates, "but you also have the datum of your own existence, your own inner being, which, as Kierkegaard and others pointed out, should be taken into account too.

"Kierkegaard spoke of the Leap of Faith. Faith is faith. You're not going to be able to repose in it because if it were obviously true, it wouldn't be faith. If God were provable, he would be kind of an oppressive tyrant who would always be there. There's no getting around it; you have to believe, even against the grain of reason."

Rabbit might be speaking for Updike when he observes, "Somewhere behind all this... there's something that wants me to find it." Mostly Rabbit's search for spiritual fulfillment involves unorthodox pilgrimages into sexual experimentation and other activities not generally thought of as religious. He reaches an accommodation of sorts between spirit and flesh in *Rabbit at Rest*, although readers have been reluctant to accept the character's untimely demise. Updike doesn't share their distress.

"I don't much miss him really. It's true he was a lovable character once I settled on writing about him. And he was always there for me every 10 years. But what more was left for his particular pilgrimage, after all? It seemed he had about gone the limit of his own capabilities. He is a man and all men are mortal, and therefore Rabbit is mortal. He was pretty young, but men of 56, especially overweight former athletes, die young. You see it every other week. In a way, he always lived hard and everything came to him a little too soon."

To anyone who stands across a book-signing table from him, the differences between Updike and Rabbit are immediately obvious. Unlike Rabbit, who died of too many cheeseburgers and malted milk shakes—balm for his many worries—Updike is trim and fit. He obviously has taken care of himself. Like many another writer, he has used the lives of other authors to pattern his own, but often in an inverse way. For instance, Updike is highly complimentary of Ernest Hemingway, but he claims to have deliberately set out to live and work differently from the esteemed novelist, saving his mental abilities for a stretch run in his senior years. Updike eschews strong drink, and he still puts in his hours as if he were a draftsman going to work every morning.

Noting that Jack Kerouac's *On the Road* had staked a claim to a vein in American life that said *get out, get away, make a life on the lam*, Updike consciously set out to chronicle an America that mostly stayed home and took jobs. He has not always wrestled the demons of domesticity with particular grace. He has referred to the divorce with his first wife and leaving his children as "the worst thing I ever did."

Still, he seems more at ease than his creation, the nervous, frightened Rabbit, who always has one foot out the door. In fact, Updike may be America's most well adjusted serious writer. He is mostly happy with life in America, and despite the messiness of Rabbit's pursuit of sex and wealth and other things Rabbit can't articulate, we shouldn't regard his troubles as a larger indictment of the American Way, says Updike. He thinks Rabbit's attitude, a sort of scruffy, flippant patriotism, is about right for an American Everyman (or an American writer) despite the spiritual malaise he senses.

"There has been a loss of cosmic meaning but not specifically American," Updike explains. "I think everybody to some extent feels it. Europeans, Asians, Africans too. The old gods and old verities have been questioned.

"One is living in a world where there are very few authoritative directions as to what is right and wrong, so you have to improvise, but I'm not sure even T.S. Eliot would have wanted to change his citizenship in America in the 20th century for citizenship in say, the 13th century. There was trouble there too and tremendous loss of private freedom. I don't think we realize how constrained most of the people of the past have been, how little freedom they had and how much fear was in their lives. Fear of the monarch, fear of goblins. All kinds of terror has been eased away from modern life and we shouldn't be sorry about it.

"Surely one of the most fascinating spectacles in the late 20th century is the developments in science. What will the Hubble Tele-scope tell us about deep space?" he asks rhetorically, then answers his own question. "I think it deepens the impression you already have of a ridiculously large universe from which no clear message emerges. Maybe it's a kind of primitive searching-for-God kind of mentality, but I do follow the more spectacular developments of our time with great interest. I was struck by that part of the Hubble where they trained it on a piece of blank night sky, and it turns out that the number of galaxies is almost infinite. They raised the number of galaxies to 50 billion (since then much higher—DW), a figure hard to wrap your mind around.

"We're kind of dulled to it by now. The exciting time was when Galileo put forth his theories. That was really shattering. Now we've kind of put astronomy into a corner of our minds and don't let it worry us, but it is worrisome; it does worry me. You would think that some-thing more coherent would come out of this immensity.

"I'm interested in the Hubble Telescope and I've been trying to think of some way I could use it. In the days when I wrote more light verse it would have been a good thing to write about."

Updike all but stopped writing light verse when markets dried up in the 1970s and 80s. He had always used poetry as a tool for honing language and for chronicling less weighty events in American life. Still, critics have been praising *Collected Poems, 1953 to 1993*, for lines such as these from "Academy."

> *The naked models, the Village gin, the wife*
> *whose hot tears sped the novel to its end,*
> *the radio that leaked distracting life*
> *into the symphony's cerebral blend.*
> *A struggle it was, and a dream; we wake*
> *to bright bald honors. Tell us our mistake.*

Even Updike's light verse has inspired high accolades. Take "Painted Women."

All lilac and cream and pink self-esteem
Young Madame Renoir made the sheer daylight dream;
In boas of air, without underwear,
She smiles through the brushstrokes at someone still there.

Writer X.J. Kennedy has called that Updike's best poem.

"I can't quite agree," Updike demurs. "but you're not obliged to be judgmental about your own work if you're a writer. You're only obliged to make each thing your best and exhaust all possibility of improvement as far as you can see, and then put it out there and let other people decide."

That applies to fiction as well. Most good writing is composed in part before the writer puts pen to paper, he adds, and he tends not to exhaustively rewrite.

"From what I know of other writers' habits, I would put myself in the middle of the rewriting league. I certainly rewrite more than John O'hara and Jack Kerouac and there's nothing too wrong with that. Shakespeare was another first draft writer. Ben Johnson has been alluded to as having said Shakespeare told him he never blotted a line. It might be apocryphal. I can't claim never to have blotted a line. Neither have I strenuously revised over and over again the way that Raymond Carver described himself as doing. Scott Fitzgerald was a tireless writer.

"But the structure of a thing should be complete in your head or come fairly easily. I don't think you ever revise a piece of fiction by adding characters or taking them away. You get too many rough ends or wrinkles. I believe when the inspiration seems to have stopped, you stop with it until you get charged up again. On the other hand, I'm willing to spend quite a lot of effort to get the phrasing a little better. I try to keep revising until the last proof is taken from me."

*

Updike has said story is more important than style to a work's shelf life, but he worries that writers are turning away from well-wrought coherent narratives in order to capture the dispiritedness of the times.

"I think the loss of meaning we were just discussing affects literature above all. Without there being some point to human

97

lives, why bother? What is the point of most of the fiction you read? It seems to have no point. As recently as the 19th century there was a sense of importance to being human. A kind of Providence was supposed to be watching and shaping our ends. Tolstoy and Dickens have a wonderful sense of fatedness about them, the sense of something big grinding away. It's hard to produce that now. A lot of the big writers—for instance Fredric Barthelme comes to mind and Bobbie Ann Mason—seem to be saying life is just a series of blips on the TV screen. There's a funny kind of shallowness to our experience now that it's hard to write your way around."

Still, Updike admires those who succeed. He hails the 1993 Nobel committee for recognizing Toni Morrison's fiction.

"As far as a choice goes, it was quite brilliant. It was somewhat surprising, since I've never seen Toni Morrison mentioned even as a contender. But when you think about it, she has tried to show aspects of the black experience with the kind of integrity and artistry that deserve recognition and admiration, so I don't think it's a bad choice at all. It wakes us up to the fact that there are more than just white males around."

For a self-described small town boy, Updike has proven himself capable of absorbing big time change. For instance, you won't hear him lamenting new directions in *The New Yorker*, the magazine most often associated with his name.

"*The New Yorker* is a different magazine in some ways. It's less dignified and less of a reader's magazine now. I admired its cool. You know, *You want to read? Well, here's some writing*, and they would put in these long articles without subheads or anything.

"But the editor and editors continue to print wonderful articles. There are occasionally some things now that seem quite skippable, but the poetry hasn't changed. There's more of it. I'm sorry to see the fiction reduced to one story a week, but Tina Brown had a tricky job of resuscitation. To make this magazine's charms apparent to younger readers can't be easy. *The New Yorker* that supported me for many decades is gone, but the person I used to be has changed too. Things change."

One constant in American letters has been Updike's ubiquity. He is very unlike his character Henry Beck, a Jewish writer who battles a gargantuan case of writer's block in *Beck, A Book* (1970) and *Beck is Back* (1982).

"Knock on wood," says Updike. "The fact that I write in a variety of forms helps. I can always write a book review. Certainly there's a bit of a block every day. I tend to begin the day by answering the previous day's mail, which can take a half hour. When it's at its worst however, I advise you to put down one sentence. One sentence seems to breed another and another."

In Updike's lifetime they have added up to thick layers of literary strata forming the bedrock on which his reputation lies.

He once said his short stories would be his major contribution to American letters, and collections such as *Too Far to Go: The Maples Stories (1979)*, which describes the arc of a marriage, do capture the times succinctly and tellingly. But these days, Updike points to the novels as having outpaced all his other literary entries. Which of those will survive?

"Everyone else mentions the Rabbit books, so I tend not to. I have a special fondness for the trilogy and *The Centaur*. I have a soft spot for that."

Still, Rabbit is the character who comes to mind in the ordinary reader who hears the name Updike. Neither *Memoirs of the Ford Administration* nor *Brazil* received the praise or popularity of say, *Rabbit at Rest*, and one wonders at the advisability of killing Rabbit off before what might have been a show-stopping appearance at the beginning of the new millennium in 2001. Alas, we will never know Rabbit's take on American society at the century's end unless Updike somehow resurrects him. One can imagine a magazine piece solicited for just such a purpose, but don't hold your breath.

"I don't think Rabbit would be terribly interested. I know I'm not. There's nothing quite as involving for me now as the Sixties and the Civil Rights Movement and Vietnam and Nixon's tortured fall. All that was dramatic in a way we don't see much of now. I think we're in a rather placid time which is not a bad thing. We may look back on this decade as paradise someday not too far in the future. I think Clinton is a very able president. I don't know what Harry would think about it, but I do."

Rabbit's demise, however, isn't the biggest force working against his creator's cultural significance. Updike worries that with the advent of the computer and video age, no one will be reading his books in 50 years.

"The world as it exists now is less and less print-centered. I find it hard to imagine a reversal from the trend toward electronic brainlessness. It's hard to see a return to a Gutenbergian world, although there are valiant attempts.

On the other hand, it isn't likely Rabbit will be leaving the American consciousness anytime soon. He may be through as a literary protagonist, but Hollywood has been calling. It is not the first time. *Rabbit Run* was made into a movie when it was the only Rabbit novel in existence. The *Witches of Eastwick* was a huge success, and there have been television plays, including *Too Far to Go*. Now it could be Rabbit's turn for another screen appearance.

"They've bought the rights and written a script. Whether or not it sees the screen, I don't know," says Updike. "It would be nice I guess, or would it? The money in these things isn't as great as it used to be." But there are other advantages. "If you look at the bestseller lists, especially paperback, half of them are books that there are contemporary movies out about. It's not easy to make films out of the Rabbit material. He's kind of ornery and the books pretty much depend upon the verbal envelope.

"*Rabbit Run*, made in the late Sixties sometime, came and went with tremendous speed at the box office. It was not a success, although I thought parts of the movie were very fine. It starred James Caan. His physique was not quite Rabbit's, but his face had that worried look that was good for Rabbit."

Updike smiles as he says it, the way people smile who are used to letting someone else do the worrying.

New Millennium Writings

Is pleased to present the

Obama Millennial Awards

but first... a poem by **Barack Obama,** *Pop, 102*

Winning entries appear on pages 104-111

Grand Prize Winner

Naomi Ruth Lowinsky, Pleasant Hill, CA, for her poem...
Madelyn Dunham, Passing On, 104
An American History Poem, 106

Winners

Frances Payne Adler, Portland, OR, *In the White House, 107*
Suellen Wedmore, Rockport, MA, *Because, 108*
Sarah Miller, Somerville, MA, *By Contrast, 110*

HONORABLE MENTIONS

Veda M. Ball, Boulder, CO
Craig Barnes, Santa Fe, NM
Tricia Coscia, Morrisville, PA
Deborah Cooper, Duluth, MN
Darlene Dauphin, Missouri City, TX
Terry Ehret, Petaluma, CA
Paula Friedman, Parkdale, OR
N. R. Gair, Newton, MA
Darryl Halbrooks, Richmond, KY
Maryanne Hannan, Delmar, NY
F. Gerald Jefferson, Cleveland, TN
Langston Kerman, Ann Arbor, MI
Ann Killough, Brookline, MA
Andrew Lam, San Francisco, CA
Herbert Lowrey, Washington, DC
Barbara March, Cedarville, CA
SheLa Morrison, Gabriola Is., BC
Garrett Rowlan, Los Angeles, CA
Jesse Tangen-Mills, Bogota, COL
Diana Whitney, Brattleboro, VT

Barack Obama
Pop

Sitting in his seat, a seat broad and broken
In, sprinkled with ashes,
Pop switches channels, takes another
Shot of Seagrams, neat, and asks
What to do with me, a green young man
Who fails to consider the
Flim and flam of the world, since
Things have been easy for me;
I stare hard at his face, a stare
That deflects off his brow;
I'm sure he's unaware of his
Dark, watery eyes, that
Glance in different directions,
And his slow, unwelcome twitches,
Fail to pass.
I listen, nod,
Listen, open, till I cling to his pale,
Beige T-shirt, yelling,
Yelling in his ears, that hang
With heavy lobes, but he's still telling
His joke, so I ask why
He's so unhappy, to which he replies...
But I don't care anymore, cause
He took too damn long, and from
Under my seat, I pull out the
Mirror I've been saving; I'm laughing,
Laughing loud, the blood rushing from his face
To mine, as he grows small,
A spot in my brain, something
That may be squeezed out, like a
Watermelon seed between
Two fingers.
Pop takes another shot, neat,

Photo by Lisa Jack

Points out the same amber
Stain on his shorts that I've got on mine, and
Makes me smell his smell, coming
From me; he switches channels, recites
An old poem
He wrote before his mother died,
Stands, shouts, and asks
For a hug, as I shink,* my
Arms barely reaching around
His thick, oily neck, and his broad back; 'cause
I see my face, framed within
Pop's black-framed glasses
And know he's laughing too.

* "Shink" may be a typo, but the poem is reproduced as published.
* Students under the tutelage of journalist Steven Barrie-Anthony, of
Occidental College, discovered this poem in an Occidental College Lit
Mag of 1982, when Obama was a student there, prior to attending
Columbia. They subsequently appeared in Occidental Weekly, before
Anthony posted them on the Huffington Post website in March, 2007.
Read more at www.huffingtonpost.com/steven-barrieanthony/obamas-
poetry_b_44271.html

Naomi Ruth Lowinsky

Madelyn Dunham, Passing On *

> *A wind blows when we die*
> *For each of us owns a wind*
>
> **~ Xan**

I never knew I'd be wind, when I died—a warm wind
on my way home from the islands—a light breeze

off the lake—breath in my grandson's lungs
as he speaks to the crowds on this—

his election night. Does he know this is me—
touching his face and the faces of those who never believed

they'd see the day. Who'd have thought I'd be breath
in the bodies of so many strangers; who'd have thought I'd be music,

sweet as the sound of the slack key guitar, or that I'd become
an ancestral spirit in the land where they know how to feed

the dead—they're roasting four bulls, sixteen chickens,
some sheep and goats, to feast the one

who belongs to us all—to the Kenyan village
of his grandmother Sara, to the spirits of his father and mother, his black

and white grandfathers, to the ones who are laughing and crying in Grant Park.
In the land of the dead— nothing is over—we still wander, still worry

take pleasure, make trouble, demand our portion
of beer, of drumming, of dancing all night. I say to you living—

though I've drifted away, though I'm only a sigh—an ex–
halation—I can feel your whole world shift—

though I'm only the faraway sound
of a slack key guitar…

---

* *Madelyn Lee Payne Dunham, Barack Obama's maternal grandmother, was born in 1922 and died on Nov. 2, 2008, just two days before Obama won the election. She was a bank vice-president in Hawaii. Obama said that when he was a child, his grandmother 'read me the opening lines of the Declaration of Independence and told me about the men and women who marched for equality because they believed those words put to paper two centuries ago should mean something.'—Wikipedia on 'Obama's Family.'*

'There is a place in poetry where the spiritual and the political meet. In the "Deep River" Writing Circle I lead at the SF Jung Institute we visit that place, read poems aloud, and write under their influence. It was there that a phrase from a South African aboriginal poem—"a wind blows when we die"— captured me. It was there that the spirit of Obama's grandmother came to me. Politics is a life and death matter in my history—my parents fled Nazi Germany. I feared a slide into fascism during the Bush years. As I watched Obama on TV, speaking to the crowds in Chicago after

his election, I realized how grateful I am for an unassuming woman's love for her grandson. The Obamas' home is not far from my mother's in Hyde Park. I know Chicago weather—that mean wind from the lake. A balmy breeze on a November evening? What else could that be but his grandmother's wind from the islands, a wind that is changing America.'

~ Naomi Ruth Lowinsky

Naomi Ruth Lowinsky
An American History Poem

> *History is you and me*
> *History is day and is night*
> #### ~ Wally Mongane Serote

History turns us inside out
History turns us around

We were slaves in Egypt
We were slaves in Mississippi
We clung to our roofs in the flooded Ninth Ward
We walked the trail of tears

Out of Africa
Out of Russia
Out of Ireland
Out of China
Out of El Salvador

Continued...

By donkey cart
By night across borders
By raft
We children of the dark ship's hold

We who built the capital
Were kept in cages

History turned us around
Gave us another story

Beyond the rock in our bellies
Beyond the underground railway
History whispered liberty's secrets
We sang them loud

I am a Bill of Rights child
I am a black woman voter
I am the citizen daughter
Of illegal aliens
who pick your apples

They came
They became
America

History rants and raves
History pulls out her hair
History is our mad maiden aunt
She lives in the attic
We don't want to hear her harangues

We saw Kennedy fall in that car
His bright blood on Jackie's suit
We saw Martin fall
    Robert fall
    Harvey Milk fall
A thousand drink Kool-Aid in the jungle
They all fall down

We saw mountains decapitated
Frogs gone
Bees gone
Fires
Floods

In the shining city
Homes are lost
Citizens go hungry
Lives hung out to dry
    on the bottom line...

History spirals
History asks us to dance
We are gathered on the National Mall
We sit on the steps of the Lincoln
    Memorial
We are not the March on Washington
Not the Poor People's March
Not here to protest nor to petition
We organized
We walked the precincts
We voted to change America
We laugh
We weep
We take cell phone photos to update
    our face books
We tell stories of our ancestors
Who longed for this day

We belong to the ones we came in with
We belong to each other
We dance in the cold winter sun
And even we who are caught
In the Purple Tunnel of Doom
Despite tickets
Despite stories of the long hard campaign
Know our glad ship's come in

History filters our thoughts
We sit in a quiet room
With a slow clock's
Tick
Tock
And a sleeping dog

We are poets
History whispers
Liberty's secrets
We write down
Her words...

Frances Payne Adler
In the White House

January 20, 2009

Let there be sage smudged
throughout the halls
and the Oval Office
Let the windows be thrown open
and scrubbed, the curtains
washed, the floors sanded
the light bulbs changed

Let there be a grand fumigation

Let there be art
and music
coming from the out-wires
of our next world
flooding
through the windows

Let there be two young girls
after dinner after their baths
jumping on the beds
in their bathrobes
laughing.

'Before the recent
election, I had been
working with the national
coalition to impeach
George Bush and Dick
Cheney for their lies and
for disrespecting the
Constitution. It was
something I couldn't not
do. Then, when it was
clear that there were those
in Congress who were not
going to allow it, I rang
doorbells with the swelling
millions to get Barack
Obama elected. And what
a celebration, the night of
the inauguration! Yes,
that's when this poem
slipped out.'

~ Frances Payne Adler

Suellen Wedmore
Because

it has been eight years of Wall Street and Capital One
       even as the clock on the bank crashed
       and dollars morphed into coal sludge,

because levees spewed jazz
       over corpse and rooftop,
       and congress has tried to out-god
       God and

because it was eight years of platitudes:
       my fellow Americans, axis of evil,

       and the once-resilient land
       is cracked and shifting,
       because rivers steam, gulls circle
       garbage-ripe landfills,
       red-wings bathe in drainage ditches
       and we breathe air
       sans lilac, scent of pine,

because we can't afford our medicines
       and the price of broccoli is so high
       I exchanged a spinning wheel
       for a quart of milk,

because deception was the way
       to gable and yacht,

because we could choose our own
       misadventure: to catapult
       into the meandering Mississippi
       or to lie down in front of a crumbling school,

       and the Chinook salmon crept forth
       with eyes like 100 watt bulbs,

because humvees rolled over like jelly donuts
     on hot, dusty roads, and our children
     were ensconced as in a shooting gallery
     at the county fair,

because guns pinged their warnings
     in a Texas drawl,
     and headlines screamed of suicide bombs
     and post traumatic stress syndrome, on

January 20th, 2009,
     honesty opened
     its big umbrella,
     discourse grew ruffle-edged,
     conjugated, and serene.

We found a map
     with the roads named and numbered—
     it will be a long trip
     and some of the bridges
     are not even built,
     but we can sense the continent
     stiffening beneath our boot-clad feet;

in the editorials
     in the *New York Times*
     there are more wildflowers
     and fewer axes,

and today we can skip around
     the Eiffel Tower
     wearing stars and stripes on our Izod shorts.
     The Germans offer up *calzones,*
     the Italians hand out strudel,

and the Republicans
     begin spelunking
     a vacant song.

'Most important to my growth as a writer has been my regular partici-pation in workshops. I am a member of two wonderful writing groups: a local group where we take turns giv-ing each other assign-ments and meet bi-weekly to critique each other's work, and one in Brookline Massachu-setts with poet Barbara Helfgott-Hyett which— though quite a drive for me—I attend whenever I can for ideas, insights, advice, and support.'

~ Suellen Wedmore

Sarah Miller
By Contrast

1. *The sun sets in New England at around 3:30 PM in the winter. It is depressing. Lonely. You come to anticipate the early setting of the sun with angst.*

Each year, you get sad, pouty even, as you leave work on the first day that you realize you were, literally, at work from sunup to sundown. The sadness grows as you realize you only worked for nine hours. Even though you know it's coming, even though you are physically immersed in your memories of the year before (loud sighs, stomach aches), even though everyone else feels the same way, you still dread it. November slides away, and December drops like an anvil. It hurts. Every year. And this is what makes the dread so severe. Full understanding of what's to come always makes the dread worse.

2.

When I used to see George Bush speak, I had that same angst. This feeling set in early in his presidency, perhaps before September 11 even. Every time he stepped to the podium, I knew what was coming. I knew that he would pronounce something wrong, offend my politically correct sensibilities, or isolate a former ally with his insensitivity. And every time, he'd drop an anvil. I knew it was coming. Soon, I had to stop watching or listening to him altogether. I couldn't even watch people make fun of him. "He's just not funny," I'd say. I knew how bad it was from the beginning. The dread set in.

George Bush came to represent my personal failures. I don't mean that he represented our failures as a nation, though maybe he did. I don't mean that he represented our inabilities as a people to intellectually evolve our political processes, but maybe he did that, too. What I mean is that he represents everything I work against each day. I am a teacher.

To be sure, I am not speaking out against George Bush's intellectual failings. I don't think he is capable of the types of higher-order thinking a good leader must embody. This doesn't make me hate him. It makes me feel sorry for him. I don't look on my students who struggle with identifying themes or struggle with judgments of canonical literary figures with disgust. I scaffold their visions. I help them articulate what they can't on their own. I help them piece together their lower-order, concrete thoughts with bits of new information and skills until they can articulate more abstract concepts. Many times, I thought that what would help George Bush was just some

'Usually I don't make the space in my day or life to write. When I don't, I can tell. Things grow, thoughts push against my brain and heart until I push them out onto paper. Writing is something that I know I need, I love to do, but it's something that I don't feel that I can prioritize until I'm forced. Then, I'm awake at 2 am typing, click-clacking my husband awake. I refuse to eat or sleep until it's done (whether or not I'm done doesn't really seem to matter). "By Contrast" is the product of one of these nights.'

~ Sarah Miller

simple scaffolding. However, what George Bush got, as I understand it, was instructions.

George Bush thought like a member of a mob, made decisions based on directives, rarely asked questions, and was complacent with not knowing.

The thought that I could be contributing to creating a person of such group-think mentality, of such un-originality, of such conservative values, of such myopia, of such compliance with the status-quo, makes my stomach drop. Could I be teaching students who could one day grow up to be such a president? Doing so would mean a personal failure. Ouch. It makes my stomach ache to think about, and I sigh audibly, loudly. Winter.

3.

Sometime around March (in a good year) the sun stays out late. This will be the first day you sigh with a smile since November. You'll breathe in deep and realize that you can walk the dog *after* work. Your depression will lift and suddenly you'll start losing weight. It happens all across the region. The thinning of New England. This time of the year is not your favorite, but you appreciate it tremendously in contrast. You won't feel nervous. You won't dread nighttime. You'll realize you wouldn't notice the extra hour of light had it not been taken from you for so long. You'll be thankful. Your life is returning to stasis. A balance returns. You won't be happy forever, but you do feel like you've begun a journey towards infinite possibility. The lightness in the evening brings hope back into your life.

4.

Barack Obama makes me sigh with a smile. Perhaps in contrast anyone would cause a lessening of my political angst. But it's not anyone else. It's him. I no longer dread nighttime.

~ *Funnier than Fiction* ~
Humorous Verse by...

Ouida Williams
On Folding Underwear

I don't know why anyone should care If I don't fold my underwear.
Now I'll roll up my socks
And put 'em in a box
But I'm not gonna fold my underwear.

Now you really don't have to make your bed,
just plump up the pillows
and spread up the spread
You really don't have to make up your bed.

You really don't have to dust every day.
Just pick up the papers
and put things away.
You really don't have to dust every day.

Now I'll put up the dishes and take out the trash
and sweep the kitchen
but here's a flash
I'm not gonna fold my underwear.

And I'll put up the pans and stack up the lids
the way Mama taught us
when we were just kids
but Mama's not here and I just don't care.

And I'm not gonna fold my underwear.

New Millennium Writings

Is pleased to present the New Millennium

Poetry Awards

Winning entries appear on pages 114-121

Winter 2008-09

Ed Frankel, Los Angeles, CA, *An Altar for Uncle Joe, 114*
Wallace Stevens Joins the Justice League, 117

Summer 2008

Trish Lindsey Jaggers, Smiths Grove KY,
On the Night They Took Your Life, 119

HONORABLE MENTIONS

Summer 2008	*Winter 2008-09*
Madelyn Camrud, Grand Forks, ND	Anita Barnard, Fort Worth, TX
E.R. Carlin, Cazenovia, NY	Rhonda Bear, Hillsboro, OR
Deborah DeNicola, Pompano Beach, FL	Ellen Bihler, Hackettstown, NJ
Gary Edwards, Gardnerville, NV	Christine E. Black, Charlottesville, VA
Stephanie Elliott, Ashland, OR	Deborah Brown, Warner, NH
Gail Fishman Gerwin, Morristown, NJ	Don Hynes, Portland, OR
Carol, Gilbertson, Decorah, IA	Pat Landreth Keller, Cochran, GA
David Krump, La Crosse, WI	Ellen LaFlèche, Northampton, MA
Ellen LaFlèche, Northampton, MA	Eric Lester, Buckley, WA
Katie Letcher Lyle, Lexington, VA	Judith Ann Levison, New Hope, PA
Ken, McCullough, Winona, MN	Ellaraine Lockie, Sunnyvale, CA
Suzanne Owens, Littleton, MA	Peter Lopatin, Stamford, CT
Aliene Pylant, Flower Mound, TX	Marilyn McLatchey, Winter Park, FL
Jonathan Rice, Richmond, VA	Veronica Patterson, Loveland, CO
Barbara Smith-Alfaro, Ocean Pines, MD	Dannye Romine Powell, Charlotte, NC
Michael Sweeney, Shelton, CT	JoAnne Preiser, Needham, MA
Ruth Thompson, Colden, NY	Joseph A Soldati, Portland, OR
Pamela Spiro Wagner, Wethersfield, CT	Anthony White, San Rafael, CA
Leland James Whipple, St. Augustine, FL	Robert Williams, Pittsfield, VT
Alexandra Wild, Silver Spring, MD	Diana Woodcock, Doha, Qatar

Ed Frankel
An Altar For Uncle Joe

I put out the photograph—a Jewish Chet Baker,
your hair slicked up in a pompadour;
stone gray eyes, a soul patch like Dizzy's,
to protect your precious embouchure.
You lean on the fender of that Buick Invicta
with the overdrive and the dynaflow transmission.
My mother said you had bedroom eyes
and a cat-that-ate-the-canary smile.
Let's go for a ride, Annie.
Let's get lost.

Where do I put your perfect pitch,
the photo Tony Bennett autographed—
To the best horn player and session man in Philly.
I'll hang your hip fedora with the feather in the band
And your pork pie hat on this rusty music stand.

I wind the metronome with the mahogany front
and listen to the thick seventy eight—your solo at nineteen
on "The Boogie Woogie Bugle Boy of Company C,"
The Andrews Sisters and the Glen Miller Band.
Then some bebop, Coleman Hawkins, Clifford Brown.
The metronome ticks a hundred and twenty beats a minute,
sixteenth notes fly all over the room
at twice rate of a human heart,
the sound of your fist beating on the door that night
when you staggered through the house
into the bathroom crying, *Annie, Annie,*
and then the drop of dead weight.
My father cursed and put you on the couch.
My mother grabbed the pills from your trumpet case
while the sirens moaned to a stop outside.
The red and white lights flashed in the dark
and the neighbors came out to watch.

'To honor the memory of loved ones for the Mexican holiday, El Dia de Los Muertos, The Day of the Dead, people build altars decorated with photographs of the deceased, their favorite foods and signature belongings. Although the dead can't actually eat the food, they can take in the aromas, and if they are pleased, they will give you their blessing. It's a joyous rather than a sad holiday. "The hipster skeletons leaning on the bar," at the end of the poem echo the "calaveras" or skeleton figures drawn by Jose Guadalupe Posada that are associated with The Day of the Dead. The protagonist of the poem is based on my uncle, a jazz trumpet player from the forties and fifties.'

~ Ed Frankel

I'll skip the food; you never was much of an eater.
Where do I put the reds and whites
the uppers, downers and all arounders,
the theme-song of the man with the golden arm,
your custom-made Benge that Aunt Katy Rose
the Fishtown beauty from Kensingtown
bent over your head, and where do I put
whatever else it was that took you out of the life?
Where do I put the punch-clock job you took
with the City Department of Weights and Measures;
your heart attack, those last years, watching daytime TV.
You called it, *greasing the skids in No Man's Land.*

Continued...

...from previous page

If the smoke from my yarzeit candle could curl back in time,
I'd find that Buick Invicta and drive it back to sixties,
park it outside City Hall with the motor running.
Let's go for a ride Uncle Joe.
We'd drive straight through, coast to coast,
cat singing to Bob Wills' okey padokey Texas swing,
while we drank bad coffee from styrofoam cups.

We'd come into LA through palm tree corridors,
to the sway of second winds and start-over dreams.
When the sun went down we'd head for Central Avenue
and I'd drop you at *The Club Alabam* with Charlie Mingus,
Buddy Collette—west coast sound.
Your embouchure will come back in no time.

But truth be told, you didn't have it in you.
You would wish me well,
kiss me on the lips the way men in our family do.
I'd take you to the after-hours club across the river
where the hipster skeletons lean at the bar,
close their eyes, sitting in, laying out,
snapping their fingers, bone against bone,
Let's Get Lost.
You would stroke your soul patch and nod your head
And wait to jump into that circle of fifths
to catch up with the music again.

* Let's get lost: A Chet Baker tune.
** Yarzeit Candle: candle lit yearly on the anniversary of a Jewish death.

Ed Frankel

Wallace Stevens Joins the Justice League

I always wanted to be a member of the Justice League,
Crusading for the idea of supreme order
In a complacent world,
Even if I had to be one of those
"Who serve who also stand and wait,"
Like Lothar, Mandrake The Magician's companion,
Or Alfred the Butler, in Batman's cave.

I always wanted to make love to Wonder Woman.
She would come home after a hard day,
Peel off those high, red, boots,
Those starry shorts and change.
I wouldn't mind being the house-husband
if she would leave her wonder-bracelets on.
I would give up my position at Hartford Life,
If I could write poems like these all day long.
At night she'd slip off her bracelets
And tell me everything she'd done that day,
Stories you wouldn't believe, about the arch villains—
The Cheetah, Angle Man, The Silver Swan,
Her paper sweetheart, The pilot, Steve,
Foiling Baroness von Guenther and the Nazis,
In the DC comic books,
During the war year of nineteen forty three.

On weekends in my pied de terre in the city
She cooks casseroles of extinct and obsolescent grains,
Souvlakis, well-done lamb, and pungent cheese.
She rubs my back after we make love
And sings to me in ancient Greek
From the Orphic and Eleusinian mysteries,
Her alto voice refumed in laurel smoke
Thickened with wild honey and mare's milk.
The plays were chanted, Wallace, half-sung, you know.
I get to hear her talking, singing in her sleep.

Continued...

...from previous page

I can't disclose, as I gave my word
All the things she told me, but making love with her
Was like communications across the species.
An encounter with a Vargas calendar girl—
Rita Hayworth or Dorothy Lamour—
With inside connections to the ancient Greeks.
Her skin was cool, supple, a certain
Tensile strength, a gravity to her touch.
No subterfuge or guile, she fathomed irony
With the sense of humor of a nun,
Despite those tight and starry shorts,
Her love was dutiful but sere,
like a sybil, I suppose,
Her mind was occupied with other things.

Face up to the chances, Wallace,
She told me once,
You must go out into the world.
Your life is waiting for you.
Your wild poems will not stand in
For all you want to love.
But I would remain at the window across from the Waldorf,
Where through the chill-night reflection of my translucent self,
The city lights display like stars, above a beach,
Where Wonder Woman walks by the sea,
Trailing her magic lasso in the sand.
From the corner of my eye I see
The bat signal flash over the Gotham night
Calling in the Justice League.
I see Superman smiling at me as he squeezes
A chunk of coal into a diamond.

* *If You Can Make It So*, a book by the poet Haniel Long
* *'Your wild poems...love:' Stevens: "The wild poem is a substitute for the woman one loves or ought to love..."*
* *This poem appeared previously at Two Hawks Quarterly,*
(www.twohawksquarterly.com/category/prior-issues/)

Trish Lindsey Jaggers
On the Night They Took Your Life,

There was a ring around the moon,
and I went looking for you, outside, when the stale air inside
grew too easy, too still, and my knitting stomach
slipped its stitches.

There you were, you were,
between the old April cracks thawed
through the ground, and the stars
we'd shared since you left me, left me, left

my body. I said, "What's the matter, baby?"
and I wanted you back,
a baby, my baby—
fastened to my breast,

your breath, my life,
white drops pearled around your tiny mouth—
just so you'd believe me once again
when I say, "The world is your Milky Way."

You were there, beneath the sugar maples,
their syrups drumming against thin wood; you
cast no shadow in their shade, the moon a ring
of light at your feet.

You said, "I just need to see the earth
from the sky," and I knew
the war had sliced the moon
from your sky, shot

all the light from your stars. You were glad
to be home, on this farm, on this hill,
where the circles of night sky
meet the torn edges of land.

Continued...

...from previous page

You said, "There's a ring
around the moon," and we sat together
beneath the ring. The moon waxed colder
behind a hush of haze, threw unsteady light

on your unreadable face. I drew you close,
felt your baby ring, safe on its silver chain,
tight against my throat, said, "Talk to me,
tell me everything. Let it go."

I need to share the air, warm
as the edge of autumn—a slow-turning season,
when the pulse slows, green to yellow, to red—slow
as the syrup slipping over the edge

of your plate this morning, when I called your name,
knew from the sound of your empty bed
that the shrapnel of broken stars cut you
from me, from me, from me

'Poetry is a facet of fiction, offering a sliver of protection for the craft, too. "On the Night They Took Your Life" came from a place of pain and intolerable loss that I almost had to live with, one that others do live with daily—a pain that no one should have to endure. Only one second's hesitation and the lines between the two—can and will be irreparably smeared. A time of unwanted (and unwarranted) war brings not only the "celebrated heroes," the ones who feel they die for rights and freedoms, but also the ones who choose to die rather than kill (or because they had to kill) another human being. How are their (the latter) lives celebrated? Is suicide really a coward's way out when each of us is born with the innate responsibility and desire to keep ourselves safe and alive? No, it takes a very certain mindset to take one's own life— for any reason. However, the threads that bind each of us are so tight that it's impossible not to feel the tug of one, particularly one who chooses to let go. That tug must be the most painful to resist—or set free. Those tugs present to me the greatest challenges as a writer, as a survivor of my mother's suicide, my son's determination to end his life that way, and my determination that "this too" could—must—be overcome. To me (the poet), life—its messages, translations, and images—comes in patterns, and these patterns beg for rhythm, for substance beyond ordinary utterances. Word choices, repetitions, imagery, music and cadence are extremely important to me—as long as the meaning is clear. Poetry should not couch itself as inaccessible; otherwise, it will be lost to those who need it the most. All of us. To reach one, to tug the thread of connection to another is the ultimate goal. Or should be.'

~ Trish Lindsey Jaggers

RB Morris
flutter off

Indian summer I'd say
50 degrees or better
And the sun strolling through
A crowd of clouds still coming to us
Even as we know
It's fixing to turn a corner
And leave town
The maple tree across the street
In full glory now
A heavy golden yellow
And coming slowly down
Slow and steady
Covering the ground already
And I'm alone behind the glass
Keeping an eye on it all
As if it wouldn't take place otherwise
But of course only this little exercise
Wouldn't take place otherwise
The rest is in the cards
It's on the slate
Destined to go down
Out of my hands
But very much in my world

There they go again
A little breeze kicking up
And they flutter away
The clock is ticking on us all
What have we got?
Hard to say
Will we make it to May?
Another spring?
Another birthday?
Another dream or two
In the arms of a lover?
Another song on the radio
Passing by in another car?
Another blink of the eye
And that chilly wind
Will be at our back
Cutting us loose from all we know
Are you ready to turn colors
And flutter away?

Ruth Thompson
Speaking of the Muse

My muse comes up behind me and says
Honey
(she calls me honey)
you don't have a lot of time here
so get down—
lose the pale Flemish bride with the sidelong glances.

She says look! here I am!
dappled with oceans
furred with green and gold
honey give me your full attention here!

O she turns
light runs from her mountains like sun off bleached bone
her mangrove hair winds in a sea of stars
on the round veldt of her belly elephants graze
and at her throat lie leopards, waiting for me to come and drink.

She says you bring all those monkey voices down here
        and leave them to the leopards.

She says you work your feet down deep in my mud
suck up that ripe swamp smell of life and death
and when the leopards come for you
speak *that*, honey.
    Speak *that*.

Ruth Thompson
For Lucille Clifton

When the music starts playing
there is not a single
respectability
holds me down.

Bless Lucille's big hips
and bless my own freeatlast hips—
bless them!
Here they are moving with the music
and not worrying one bit
about where they stand in relation to anyone else.

You can look at me or not
I am not saying anything personal anymore.

I am saying hips breasts belly legs feet
roots branches and big thick trunk
tides
sunrises
monkeys lithe and witty in the dawn trees
snakes standing up and letting fall loose dry coils of humus
tigers shaking out oiled stripes of sun and shadow
frogs seeding great froths of frog spawn
and everything—
everything!—
that is not respectable.

I say you can look at me or not.
I am busy dancing
these hips feet shoulders brain heart
and there is not one perfect clean thing among them
every blessed piece of me tired worn
maculate with mistakes failures humiliations—

so here I am at last
out here boogieing—
freckled
and fond
and fat as the fat old sun.

Doris Ivie

Cantadora Sings Back Her Soul

O kinderwoman, I lost you to suburbs and deadlines and schools,
to pavement, to meetings, to email, to petty acclaim.
I choked you with girdle and pantyhose, stifled you with slips.
Now, I beckon you back. I sing you back.

O Mist Being, you are my deepest, wildest spirit.
I seek you in cathedrals of faery rings,
in kivas of mud long parched dry,
in Himalayan towns not yet on maps.

O *numina*, I dance for you, with you. I open my mouth
and our songs erupt—fiery, raging, untamed.
She-wolves howl through me and cheetahs screech your name.
In your honor I parry with men in pubs while swigging stout.

Through me you've sailed to Iona without packing a bag,
straddled logs spanning flooded Himalayan streams.
Through me you've summoned spirits in Chaco Canyon,
Felt presences in pueblos and the Great Sand Dunes.

You are the woman in me who dares to love young men and cuddle cats.
You call to me from my back yard, from fecund fields and forests.
You lure me to sacred springs to behold my gnarled reflection.
Through me you've looked seers in the eye and named them Fraud.

You chortle as I discard dozens of high-heeled shoes,
Croon as I don loud skirts, camisoles, and purple scarves.
You are my hormones, screaming to be heard—
My freedom, my future, my life.

O *dakini*, you rise within me, feral and wise.
Never again will I ignore your presence.
I will sing you until you cradle me into death.

Aliene Pylant
Gardens, 2001

July

At a going out of business sale
of oriental rugs I came upon
the piece I knew I'd buy despite the price.
Its intricate mosaic shimmered, a trail
of pearl-like saffron, turquoise, celadon
and carmine yarns, depicting primal paradise

in multitudes of flowers, leaves and scrolls.
No jarring shade or shape appeared to mar
the wool design, so soft beneath my hand.
The merchant selling the Sarouk, Abdul,
informed me that it came from far
north India, near Pakistan, a land

of mountain peaks where rabid winters stun
the countryside each year. Such killing cold
improves the Himalayan goats' fine wool,
enriching fibers shorn and dyed and spun
and woven into patterns families hold
as birthright—patterns old and valuable.

I wondered, but I did not ask, if knots
so intricate and fine were tied so snug
by children's chilled compliant fingers, skin
worn raw. Perhaps my eyes revealed my thoughts,
my guilt at wanting to possess this rug
so much that I'd dismiss its origin.

The voice of Abdul, soft as smoke, addressed
my doubts. He said that as the shuttles flew
the weavers sang—not tawdry music one would hear
on radios, but ancient chants which blessed
the fibers and the looms, and the hands which drew
and tied the threads. With song the rug appeared—

each beat became a shape, each note a hue
as artists mesmerized by melodies
describing petal curl or shade of wool

wove intricate designs completely through
surrendering to choral harmonies.
The rug became their song made visible.

September

Up from white ash ground, from gray cement,
near the smolder of the rubble, gardens grew
as hands placed bloom on bloom in cinder beds—
the white gardenias, her favorite scent;
the bachelor buttons shining piquant blue
like their father's eyes; the dozen red

and perfect roses because she loved them
and he loved her; the pristine lilies left
in angry grief; the trailing English ivy
intended for her wedding day; the long-stem
yellow roses, a daughter's hopeful gift;
the orchids from his penthouse nursery;

the piebald daisies, like his mother, sweet
and down to earth; the golden mums that lined
their front yard walk; the sprigs of innocent
sweet baby's breath. Flowers lived on deadened streets
as families, friends and strangers left behind
multi-hued bouquets in gardens of lament.

November

Fall is pushing in. My yard grows crisp
and crunchy underfoot as green retreats.
I love this time of year, the turning in
of growing things when trees and grasses slip
toward meditation, all self-conceits
abandoned. It is a time for reckoning.

Beneath my shoeless feet my rug's pashmina wool
is warm and comforting. Late afternoon's low sun
sets gold medallions on the flowers' faces
and in the passing light the rug becomes a jewel,
multifaceted and rich, a benison,
a work I treasure for its faultless graces.

Continued ...

... from previous page

I will never know the gifted artisans
whose toil delights my soul, whose work
depicts a garden scattered at my feet.
I want to think I own the blissful hymns
of weavers at their family looms and not the dirge
of homeless children forced to weave to eat.

I want to know the merchant, Abdul, closed
his doors and left as August's days were set
because his father's health was poor as I was told.
I want to trust that every fact disclosed
about the rug was not a lie. And yet
I wonder what I bought. I wonder what he sold.

As darkness sweeps in deep uncertainty
I'm comforted by Friday evening's rite—
arranging fresh-cut flowers in a crystal vase—
bursts of snow white mums and blue anemone,
stars of yellow lilies, sunlight bright
and knots of pink carnations' frilly lace.

There is no intrigue in a flower's intellect.
It knows to seek out light and follow light
and open without reticence to radiance
and thrive wind-blown, rain-wet, sun-flecked
above the soil it shivered through until frost's bite,
then spent, return to earth still rich with scent.

How can such delicate and fragile petals bear
the weight of anguish in a funeral spray
stiffening in tribute to the dead
yet carry to the altar joyful prayer
floating over blossoms of a bride's bouquet
in celebration of new life ahead.

Maybe flowers sprang from Eden's vault—
unsullied remnants of divine intent—
revealing splendor only love can bring—
which harbors sorrow for all human fault
while honoring a fragrant covenant
to bloom anew for us each coming spring.

Ellaraine Lockie

Coming Home in a Haibun

Sixteen miles south on Highway 87 the road turns a sharp corner east.
And the first head-on view of the blue green purple Bear's Paw range
grabs me. Right in the solar plexus.

> Bright sun on mountains
> Cotton ball clouds dance colors
> over the prairie

Then the small death. The ascension of a year's worth of city.
A bear hug that squeezes every tight muscle, nerve and tendon
until they loosen into a pulled-pork state.

> Pronghorn antelope
> bound away in ballet leaps
> Wheat and wild grasses

I open the car door at the cabin and walk into stillness. Not even the
cottonwood leaves quiver. Light has become a tarnished film.
Meadowlarks and crickets occupy the airwaves in fast forward tempo.

> Gun metal gray sky
> Ants crawl underground to homes
> with soil high entries

Horses roll vowels from deep within their bellies. We all know
what's coming. I grab a can of cat food from a grocery sack. Head
for the barn my father built, to interfere with survival of fittest laws.

> A thick dark curtain
> drops in front of the Bear Paws
> Distant drum rumble

I sit on the porch swing by ponderosa pine cones budded
in pink nipples. Watch the swell of lilac blooms in smells and shades
of childhood. Breathe in the aged cedar of the cabin.

> A soft rippled song
> from the cottonwood branches
> Muted wind whistle

Blue spruce boughs rise and fall in patterns like pedals on an organ.
The sky explodes in a white wrath. I offer a prayer. Wait for the fallout.
For the cleansing. The renewal.

Winner of the Illinois State Poetry Society Contest, Formal Poetry Division

Rhonda Bear
The Red Clay Pot

Somewhere over there on Bear Mountain,
you might come across a red clay pot, simple and round,
filled with a child's collection of plain, gray river stones,
a handful of sand, crispy brown spider skins,
a perfectly round nest of twigs,
and a solitary black feather fallen from an eagle's wing.

Among the ruins of intentions,
in a place as high as hopes,
it rests,
so near to the awesome blue infinity,
so achingly far from the cherished riverbed
of its beginnings.

If you were to open its lid on a fragrant mountain morning,
a recollection of swaying cottonwoods
and the cool, green, slippery pleasures of high spring waters
might stir in the sand, and soothe the parched stones.
The spider skins might dance a little half-remembered weaving waltz,
and spin stories of brief rainbows captured in drops of morning dew.
The nest might soften inside, recalling tiny feet
and sweet, small voices.

But the black feather would surely awaken
at the sun's warm touch,
and rise trembling from its bed of stones
to feel the familiar fingers of the beckoning breeze.
And then the long silence of separations would be broken
by the snap of spreading wings.

Ellen Bihler
Red Barns

I like the inevitability of rural decay—
wood and nails vs. time and weather,
and the personage inside the platitude,
weathered red barn:
missing patch of tar roof shingles,
north-winded tilt to the right,
tic-tac-toe of window panes.

I like the ancient, empty ones best—
angles all askew, paint stripped away in blotches
as if the hand that held the red crayon
wandered before completing the page.
Barren door and window frames
let the wind blow through, front to back.
In the soupy dark, stray bits of hay and dust
swirl alongside ghost-sounds:
a bray, a whinny, a booted footstep.

When I am very old, prop up my body
deep in some farmer's field,
my skin taut over bones
tenacious as wood posts.
Paint me red barn red and tell the wind
to hollow out a place inside, deep
enough for a long forgotten song.

'Red Barns' previously appeared in Late Summer Confessions, Pudding House Press, 2009.

Christine E. Black
To Dust

I thought this poem
had to have everything
in it to earn its existence,
the ultimate argument,
brick by steady brick
in rows, thick text
fortress against
waves of dismissal,
derision's sneer,
or before the violent
muscular roar
with chrome gleaming
hard like the surface
of a lie.

If it were not
gun metal tight
like the barrel
of a shot gun,
then knife words,
slippery verbs
may find an opening.

But now I know,
this diaphanous phrase,
ambiguous word
caresses white space,
a girl's hair
not shrouding
her face.

And look, this sentence
unravels like a veil,
dusk softening the right
angles of a cross.

Spidery roots
split rock, grip cliffs.
This poem falls
loosely from the page,
hushes like steady rain
through which a mountain
turns to dust
before our eyes.

Madelyn Camrud
The Pulse

Some day one of us will look back to this,
the rain outside the glass,

the two of us under the covers.
One will look back to warm arms, kisses,

tongues, lips, but will not get
the moment back, not the way it is now;

it will be like this morning's dream,
so close in my mind, but gone. Some day,

after death has come singing between us,
one of us will try to recapture

the smells we know now. One will remember
the rain, how it came before we heard it

and we awoke knowing only its sound
on the pane, listened as closely

as a bride in her chamber
for her husband. One of us,

eyes closed, will try so hard to see
the other, will try to remember

arms, legs enmeshed,
our breaths, hearts, together:

three, four, five, six,
and farther, and the two of us,

like the rain, falling
deeper, into the singing.

*'The Pulse' previously appeared in Madelyn's chapbook, **The Light We Go
After**, Dacotah Territory Press, 2007.*

Marilyn Kallet
That Chicken

~ *Auvillar, 2009*

Was a senior citizen
an octogenarian
the oldest one in Valence d'Agen.
That chicken's skin was so thick
it couldn't be insulted.
Nothing could hurt it, not even a knife.
That chicken was so old it knew my Grandma Anna in Minsk.

That chicken was so tough
even the boiling water complained.
That chicken wasn't worth 15 Euros.
15! That chicken was tougher than the pot,
tougher than the teenage boys who rumbled last night by the dock,
and much less sexy.

That chicken was one of two on Noah's ark.
I ate it because I paid for it.
Each bite was an insult.
That was the chicken they saved for the American.
That was the chicken that broke détente.

I made a soup of it,
and with enough hours and white wine
even the oldest clucking citizen of the republic
gave way to my teeth.
With a loaf of olive bread to distract me
I polished off that beast.
But was it a chicken or a buzzard?
Je m'en fous! For fifteen Euros I'd eat a hedgehog
if it came home in my shopping bag.
I'm no spring chicken
but I'm livelier than that old bird.

Love Poem for the Ageless

If we were ageless and wore no bodies, we could rendezvous on a slip
of light, a firefly's back—who would begrudge us
and my face wouldn't crack—

No more death mask jokes no more crawling things
escaping, what are these—words?
Blows.

Who crumbles from them? Not Ozymandius,
not any object, past or present.
Me, my pretensions, who did I think I was.

I'll be out of time
soon enough
stick to that, that time of year

bare.
If we were ageless, bodiless,
outside ourselves,

we'd meet like this, in words
pinpricks of light—
the other real,

almost-flesh

E.R. Carlin
In the Closet of the Steel Museum

Beyond the hall of photographs, the inscriptions shining gold,
the closet door unlocked, I discovered

the modern workers' equipment: five hoagie-shaped sweepers
all with dislodged handles like torpedoes,

there was an arsenal of window cleaner, and an ant motel
in the corner. As Heather and I slipped inside,

I thought of my grandfather's broken watch. His refusal
to take it off, even in the light of criticism.

The first time he brought me here, he invested hours explaining
the production of steel. His wristwatch

shined like a beacon to my boredom. All I wanted then
was to be out strumming my alternative

tuned guitar under the pine trees, dreaming of easy nymphets
with lilac perfume and black lipstick.

My grandfather ended his story by demonstrating how he
dipped his fist into a bucket of hot water

on the day U.S. Steel shut down forever. He held his branded arm
under until the second hand on his watch

stopped. His face flushed red; I understood this not as salient
anger but as a lack of oxygen, an eroticism

for the strange landscape of life lived. At that moment I
dipped my hand under her skirt, pulling

her body up against mine, her lips to my lips. I could smell
her black hair, not like lilacs at all, but

like burnt waffles, the kind he and I made when nine-inch snow
boxed us inside the apartment complex.

And here we were, crammed like a bookmark into an encyclopedia
of the real thing. I thrust and held my

breath until climax. Sharing last heats long into the glow of after-hours,
the light dimmed and I scurried out the front door

as the security officer bellowed after me. For him the nightshift
was just beginning. For us, it ended a lifetime ago.

In the cold dark, I remember that night as steam climbing out of sewer
grates, as a rash of thought in a depression of flesh.

Deborah Brown
String Theories

I am responsible for scraping the daylight
   along the silver edge of the moon
      with my fist. I say nothing

about how fast the light travels
   or of Einstein's problem catching up with it,
      or of Ludwig Boltzmann, who killed himself

when scientists mocked his belief
   in other dimensions. Today
      the strings of Boltzmann's theory

have stories to tell, they
   pulsate to anyone's rhythm.
      I hold you in ten dimensions,

wish you safe in all of them.
   I know space and time curl around strings
      that give rise to the gravity

which holds us here, the way the notes
   of Mozart's Requiem scrolled
      on his last staves. The invisible strings

of each of us spin themselves into specks of light,
   and two new forces one strong and one weak,
      draw us together. This is the complicated

shape of our time together, our past and present
   woven into a fragment of the sky.
      Every poem is an elegy to you.

Deborah DeNicola
Sun Song

I drag my chair to the water's edge and marvel
at the sea's interaction with my footprint. I pledge
my mark on earth, awash in a new shape. And I thank
the sun that charges the sand, charges landscape,

fuses clouds to their densities, fissioning color.
It's the beginning of rhythm, percussive shimmy and pulse,
that ballet of lift-to-rise within the sky's furnace that contains
the history of music as well as stewing codes of global light.

Wasn't it the sun that gave birth to creation? The spark
at the center that *waah-waahed* into the Bang—vertical
membranes stringing illusion of linear time, earth's heating,
her spirals spinning, her platelets…. It's the sun

that choreographs our color, our out-takes and inscapes.
Ancient Egyptians succumbed to its gnosis, swarmed
on their knees to greet the atoms stirring open
each day. It began with Thrice Great Hermes, his arcane

alchemy: a young boy's urine, the Pelican's capacious jaw,
promises spawned from a low blown digeridoo deep
respirations of light, maracas of morning's scrawling caws—
And did our first ancestors drum to synchronize our DNA

so we'd perceive collectively in awe? For millennia earth
preceded human presence, so much mystery before the knowns…
The proto-consciousness shift to subjective awareness
and the same sun like a monolith overseeing Trojan

and Peloponnesian wars. Caesars fancied themselves
the sun's descendants before the Vikings and Huns,
Goths and Visigoths called it a masculine star. Arrogant,
overbearing. And to the more soft-sided, in-sighted…

Eric Lester
Blushed

Blushed with dawn's skin, blooded cold,
I watched Earth's star drawn to her face,
cloud-tressed coquette alluring bold
his fusion fire-gaze heat from space.
He bathes her form with kindling grace,
though she has turned her cheek away,
and shy, a lash of fir tips trace
chart lines against the china day.
What words will these old lovers say,
while they conceive the morning's light,
the murmur of their ancient play
twined out and in until the night.
Her oceans fill with frothy life
as Sunlight smiles upon his Wife.

(read *Female*, read *priestesse* or *witch*)... just a blossom
of wisdom and oxytocin. If the sun were mine,
I wouldn't freeze it in photographs but keep it coming,
becoming—a model, Messiah, a husband with whom to slip

into corners and caves where candles ignite and cobwebs
are swept to make room for merciful warmth. And so often,
of course, light triggers the inner antennae of bird lore,
rumored as Nature's Keeper, this sun, *our* sun. After all,

we too are heliotropic, round and around. *I feel therefore I turn
toward light.* Let shine sing a capella in the sussurus of ocean.
And I open my languorous mouth to the Gregorian,
tropical dusk. Rhythmic bodies catapulted from

moonless galaxies into dawn. The sun is a song!
It trails off as I swallow the light. It fills the air
and scatters... like nano seconds in timelessness,
flesh and fire to dust.

Gary Thomas Edwards

Unbridled passion the legacy of man, once past the bubble, travels the universe forever

The tall timber lightly listed,
and the old man, shutting down his menacing saw
with a flick of his thumb took several steps back
as the crisp crack
resonated through the entire forest
permeating all with its clarity.

The solid spruce boldly called out one last time
with a significant roar rushing headlong toward the ground
to embrace a new path, a new journey.
The old man, feeling a tinge of remorse,
wiped the sweat from his forehead
as he walked slowly over to the fallen giant.

Timbre will leave the land, follow man, follow Voyager I and II
Hindered not by mass,
it will cross the outermost,
transverse the heliospheric bubble,
where the solar winds will blow

At the mill, another man, a caring man
gently runs his hand along the smooth tight grain.
He smiles, and the craftsman's eye gleams.
This was a fine piece of wood, he thought to himself.
A caring man he would take this wood home.
He would give this wood life

With the care and passion of Cristofori of Italy,
the craftsman let lay his patterns on the wood,
carefully tracing there every nuance and subtle curve.
He will pour his very soul into this wood
to give it life
as so many he has before

Timbre will leave the land, follow man, follow Voyager I and II
Hindered not by mass,
it will cross the outermost,
transverse the heliospheric bubble,
where the solar winds will blow

Iron, carbon and silicon, carbon steel glowing bright
radiance of the sun as it pours into the sand, into the cast
so much stronger this way
for it is so that
longer pianos with longer strings
have better sound and little inharmonicity

Delicious, lustrous layers of satin black
lay on thick, gleaming like candy
sealing tightly a hardened finish.
The master's hands polish brightly
every metric measure of
this his tour de force

Timbre will leave the land, follow man, follow Voyager I and II
Hindered not by mass,
it will cross the outermost,
transverse the heliospheric bubble,
where the solar winds will blow

In the artist's room
dark and filled with creative gloom
she searches hard for but a single note.
It must follow an accidental sharp
stepping up a single semitone
and help to match her soulful moan

Her fleshy fingers tease and
then appease hitting hard the ivory keys
striking felt hammered chords
vibrate then you steely strings
and bring to life
the timber's dreams

Timbre will leave the land, follow man, follow Voyager I and II
Hindered not by mass,
it will cross the outermost,
transverse the heliospheric bubble,
where the solar winds will blow

Anita Barnard
Building with Straw

I think I'll live lightly
on the earth.
The trees will be welcoming;
spiders will be friends.

If I build my house of straw,
my walls will be thick, comforting,
the sun will be my ally in winter,
in summer, the cool of earthen floors.

This is what I have:
wildflowers,
thorns of mesquite and a newborn orchard;
a misery of chiggers,
the call of coyotes as dusk falls,
121 acres and one outhouse.

We sleep in tents
in the Texas heat, when school
has released us.
My escape from chaos and concrete.
Cool of evening falls faster in the country.
The moon rises,
and we join the howl.

I want to build a house.

I've been collecting tools,
the well-weighted hammer, level, miter saw,
sketching plans.
Stacks of papers bloom
with the grove of cabins I want to raise, shelters
small and friendly to the land
and all the friends and dreamers I want to gather there.

Continued...

Dannye Romine Powell
It Is Harder To Keep You Out of My Thoughts

than it is to play the Japanese game
of tearing paper into the shapes of butterflies
and floating them onto the air, fanning
to make them light on a bouquet of peonies
on the piano across the room,
then fly away, light once more,
as if they were winging in the garden,
allowing not even one to drift to the ground.

We stretch out on the ground, beckoning sleep,
full with the smell of the dying fire
and echo of song,
and deep dreaming breaths of my daughter
in her little sleeping bag,
sharing air with the grasses.
Before I sleep, I drink in her peace.
I rest my hand on her warm skin.

I'll live on the land, grow berries,
eat peaches, nurture art,
pause at the huff and puff
through the handmade sill,
wind parting around straw walls.

The wolf will come;
I'll put my fingers in his hair.

Gail Fishman Gerwin

Around the Corner from Twelfth

Paterson, 1939-1952

Around the corner from Twelfth
in the middle of the block stood
the house on Madison Avenue,
>   worn grey shingles, planked porch,
>   summer chairs overlooking
>   the stream of crosstown traffic.

On the right, the house where the woman
everyone called Grandma Decker
lived with her daughter.
>   The alley just wide enough to hold
>   my sixth grade boyfriend who could
>   whinny like a horse, growl like a cur,
>   bay like a moonstruck wolf,
>   spurring Mama's giddy laughter.

Across a wide driveway
in the house on the left,
widowed Mrs. Wilkes
still hanging out laundry for two,
>   her clothesline stretching across
>   a deep yard where snowfalls of
>   springtime pear blossoms tickled
>   my arms, garnished my spiral curls.

Outside my bedroom window,
my father's trucks, J. Fishman and Son,
Moving and Storage, Maine to Florida,
open rear doors facing the brick warehouse,
its mysterious interior forbidden.
>   The furniture men—Reggie, Freddie,
>   Toothless John—hoisted, toted, stacked,
>   laughing, smoking, from dawn 'til sundown.

In our first floor flat
my mother tended the black phone
in the office, a tiny stall off
the dimly lit living room.
   The dining room's bay window sill
   a stage for impromptu acts,
   my waving arms and tapping feet
   entertaining me from the gilded mirror
   on the opposite wall.

In the back yard, feral cat packs
howled, yowled, birthing an
endless inventory of striped, calico,
   witchcraft black kittens, morning beggars
   under the pantry window awaiting
   my mother's daily scrap ration.

Two doors up the street,
Nancy Watson, fearsome blonde bully,
called me *dirty Jew dirty Jew*,
   called my beating heart black,
   encircled me with her allies,
   singing *Jesus Loves Me*.

Across the street the Karr girls,
unwashed hair, dirty dresses,
a mother who brought home a different uncle each night.
   When they disappeared
   my mother said they'd been taken,
   sent to the orphanage on Eleventh.

Continued...

...from previous page

Around the corner on Twelfth
next to the Esso station,
bearded Gus sold comic books,
ten cents to follow antics
of Betty, Veronica, Archie.
        Toupéed Aaron sold vegetables,
        he cheated people, Mama said.
        The tavern at Twenty-second
        harbored daytime drinkers,
        street stumblers stirring terror,
        don't cross there, she warned.

The house on Madison Avenue,
early childhood haven,
square yard collecting blizzards,
kitchen warm with soothing odors,
birthday parties in May.
        When autumn came Mr. Walfish
        from upstairs built a succah outside,
        ate his meals under a ceiling
        of branches strung with fruit.

The avenue fostered peril,
haughty Nancys, leering Esso men,
uneven sidewalks tripping tricycles,
skinned knees, tears, my mother's refrain,
I told you so I told you so.

        Around the corner from twelfth
        stands the house on Madison Avenue,
        a rusted truck with no wheels
        in the driveway.

Stephanie Elliott
What the Tattoo Artist Said

Sometimes it's tempting to spell a lover's name wrong,
especially when they've already got the portrait
of an ex inked on their shoulder.
While cutting through the cemetery going to work today
I thought about other unfortunate intimacies:
a customer with Frankenstein on his forearm,
and others united with maniac chainsaws, snarling guard dogs,
revolvers, robots, or barcodes. I always remind them,
saying, you're choosing what you never have to let go,
what you'll feel closer to,
what you might become.
Like in that Oliver poem
where she lies down to think about death
but instead falls asleep in a field of flowers.
The one where she wakes up covered with wet petals
and wrapped up in vines, feeling so close to that boundary
where her body becomes the plants she's tangled in.
Once I spent days wrapping
a man's arms in purple tentacles:
at least the angelheaded hipsters
know what's worth longing for.
They come in to be covered
in lilies, butterflies, and birds—
but does it get them any closer
to that lush, ravenous world?
Can these plants in fixed bloom
or these flat frescoed feathers
take us in? While pressing an owl into
a woman's shoulder
I remembered a time when I was a kid
that a crow would tap at the bedroom window.
I left it open once and waited
and for just a moment
he stepped inside.

Renee Epling
Alchemist

Illuminate me with your light!
In your dark eyes
reflection enhanced
base morsel of Earth, disguised
becomes a jewel
luminous
wondrous
intense
opal.
Bathe me in your light!
By your hand, within this gem
fires ignite
prisoned in its heart
promises of beauty hold
flashes
lightnings
dazzle
glow.
Dare, lest you invoke regret!
Taste forbidd'n fruit your alchemy has
    wrought
Sorcerer, plumb its secret depth.
Private mysteries await
your master key;
unlocked
pursued
audacious
free…

Carol Gilbertson
Birds

After months without song
or sight of wing,
I sweep aside the curtains
and suddenly one stops
on the winter-bare honeysuckle
inches from the window.
Then, as if arranged,
another lands just below.

They sit on their twigs,
facing different directions
without speaking,
and yet each delicate body
seems to ruffle slightly.

Sometimes
in the living room at night
when you and I sit
faced into different books,
one lamp-lit body
shifts slightly in its chair,
sensing across the room
the other's warmth,
the soft flight within.

Leland James
Dreamscape

at the end of the magnolia
there's a window on a garden
there a spirit bird is singing
he is dreaming of the garden

in the garden is a woman
she is calling to a madman
through the window on the garden
where the spirit bird recites

now the spirit bird is waking
soon the garden will be over
the magnolia was the woman
and the madman was the song

> as the spirit wakes it flies
> the madman sleeps
> the garden fades
> the magnolia petals fall

the window now is broken
like the woman in the garden
like the madman through the window
like a   caterpillar's shell

a butterfly is crying
he is dreaming of the garden
through the   broken window
the magnolia woman weeps

Don Hynes

What May Fill the Human Heart

The rituals of war
are the altar sacrifice
of our collective confusion.
We think to put a bloody ram
upon the broken table
thinking the blade and the blood
will give us merit with the God
we have forgotten.
No remembrance comes
from this pointless sacrifice,
no feeling from the recurring violence,
only the increased numbing
of our once rich and fertile hearts.
The argument, the altar, the sacrifice,
these are the instruments
of the delusional priesthood,
the deceptive magicians
who steer our misbegotten course.

Deep in the mountain
there is a creek winding back
to a green and fertile canyon
abandoned by the merchants and slavers,
producing nothing worthy of sale
except ancient trees set in glacial silt,
rooted down to middle earth.
In that forgotten place
where the creek runs cold and brilliant
She awaits the lover She lost
when the Earth shifted
and he became dupe to the engines of war.
She knew his once bright fire
and is not fooled by what he has become.
She rests in her obscurity,
the cedars and firs Her guardians,
the rocks and flowing water

Her touch stone and glimmer
of continuing presence.
She waits the time foretold of his awakening
amidst the bloody remains
of his brutal and ignorant practice.
She knows the greater Light is needed
and She feels that stirring in Her soul,
sending a message to all Her frightened children:
"The Light is returning, the Light!
Now may he awaken and allow his love for Me
to once again fill his heart."

The human world knows little of this prayer
and less of the sacred place where it is spoken,
yet the magic of incantation has its way;
as the wages of war diminish,
the bankruptcy and dawning light
combine to bring new awareness.
In the quietness of this sacred moment
between what was, what is and what is yet to be
the wholeness of creation takes a first new breath.

Judith Ann Levison
Last Act

I did not want to grow this old.
More questions than answers.
The big one like the moving colors
Of a garnet is abstract yet yearns
For my lost attention to its
Black-blood brilliance resetting.

I tap my cane upon stone,
Hoping it will pierce then tarnish
The lament of my generation, mad
With gossip, our hats pinned to our hair
Never to be loosened by wild wear.

It startles me to now desire passion,
Now when life, a ritual of bowl, soap, and bed,
Sees the clarity of love
Become the magic of real things:
Dusk before a velvet-antlered dark,
Jagged rows of rocks you want to
Follow to a clot of daisies at the end.

What truth to see the wrinkling and
Fanning of the butterflies
In painted colors dance, then breathe
And mock my frequent and awed search
For the rippled swirling of my skirt
Brought to the lips, click, click!

I do not know how to prepare for death.
Local eyes say: *see her now, then you won't.*
Somewhere as night comes on, like a slipper pat, patting,
I am now alone in a patio, sipping rum and coke,
Thinking this a proper ending, or a beginning
As when I first jumped into flour-sifted snow.

'Last Act' previously appeared in Iconoclast, #98, 2008

Peter Lopatin
You Are Here

and it is now, that's all
you know. Attend to it.
Give the present its due.
The shadow cast by the
woman standing there,
waiting for the cars to pass,
subtends a certain angle
on the grass. Take note of it.
Give the present its due.

The bus arrives, departs,
takes passengers vectored
to other parts. An old man aboard,
on his last trip home, sees his
granddaughter laugh and
wave him gone. He fixes the
image fast in his mind and
gives the present its due.

At the edge of a field,
three Amish men consider
what to do: wait for the rain,
then plant, or plant and
wait for rain. The young ones turn
to the older man, certain he'll
know what to do. It strikes them
as odd when he stares at the bus,
giving the present its due.

If you find yourself at
your walk's end, where
the trail narrows in the
undergrowth, your choices—
once multiple—may seem
pitifully few: turn back
before night falls, or just
hack your way through.

But consider choice 'c':
let the undergrowth beguile you.
Stay where you are and
give the present its due.
Let 'a' and 'b' fight it out alone
and do the heavy lifting
without you.

Take yourself to be no more
than some elusive *'who'*—
a traveler still, though at rest.
Attend to the arc of the afternoon.
Give the present its due.

*Peter Lopatin accepts his Honorable
Mention on condition that NMW notes his
objection to the Obama Millennial Award
presentations herein. So noted.—DW*

Marianne Chrystalbridge

Inheritance

This antique rocker
began where sunlight in dusty columns
illuminated the craftsman,
back hunched in cobwebbed window,
summer-heated barn in Connecticut,
fragrance of woodshavings, hay and manure.

Wood sanded and buffed to molasses brown,
he fashions his yearning for waves
(a day's journey then, to the shore)
into curlicues at the arm rests,
his memories of closer places—
mirrored lake, wing-curve of wild duck,
scattered droplets in flight—
in the arc above the headrest.

When horses plodded down Main Street,
Grandma, young then and lithe,
dipped water from the well by the garden.
The rocking chair creaks now—
I stuff wood shims against the pegs to quiet the creaking.
Rockers, braces, all upturned surfaces gather dust
except those sheened surfaces where our bodies touch,
strands on backrest and seat, the shade of my young daughter's legs in July,
recaned by a man in Tennessee (a summer month's journey from Connecticut
then), his hands woven into its history, his work
a traditional pattern of holes
small enough to encircle the fingers.

Memories of my grandparents' farmhouse,
where creaking floors rhymed with creaking chairs,
illuminate this old construction.
In my living room now, the chair is a silent sun-browned native
until someone enters the realm
of person and chair,
animating the sphere with stories—*and then I...*
mumbling sleepily... *coffee?*
gazing quietly into the fire, breathing,

Continued

154

Ouida Welch Williams
The last time you kissed me

You said my name and *kiss me*.
I went to you, leaned in to you
and we kissed—twice—and then
I held your hand till it was over
and you were
                        gone.
leaving so many
sweet kisses over the years....

Soft kisses, eager kisses
hungry kisses
                        goodbye
kisses
hello kisses
making up kisses
I never got tired of kissing you.
                        I'll always love you.

To the Memory of Ladonuel Williams, 1924-
1985. Don of the Gospel duo Don and Earl.

turning the page, push
with the foot, creak,
push, sighs
bored, satisfied,
sexual or tender,

My mother rocking me,
me rocking my babies in turn,
singing "goodnight my sweetheart,
goodnight my love,"
my lullabies sung to the rhythm
of the rockers against the floor
and the creaking I could not silence.

Pat Landreth Keller
Not for Publication

Really, nobody's drinking.
We're on the phone talking about *Poetry*,
his chances of breaking in, and I'm a believer.
This guy is good, solid,
five books out already, but he's saying,
"*Poetry* publishes almost nothing that they get,
and I've been sending poems to them since 1958,
since I was 19, and I'm getting *old*."

"Me too," I say.
Then I remember my friend can't use a computer,
thanks to poverty and chronic pain,
like John McCain can't use a computer because of torture,
so there we are, my friend and I, ironing out the details
of his future *Poetry* submission via me, on my computer,
while I'm thinking my friend, being a liberal,
might not like the comparison, even if McCain *is* military,
but not a former Marine, like my friend.
On the other hand, a few weeks ago
we heard an English professor say, in twenty years
Roethke would be dropped like a rock from textbooks.
We both breathed sorrow into the summer air;
we both felt tortured, though I not physically.

My friend, though, suffers every day,
so I had meant to tell him about my father,
who had suffered in a different way,
in the Merchant Marine in the Arctic,
at the wheel of his ship after a torpedo attack.
Another ship had gone down. Dad was turning his ship
to avoid the wreckage, and the waters were awash
with arms and legs, and blood and ice,
and he couldn't change his course or slow the ship
to try to save all those men in the water.

Then the screaming stopped, and the men sank,
but the ships' engines never quit turning
as the convoy, unarmed, tried to run for it,
unable to throw out lifelines, not knowing
when or where the submarines might fire again;
besides, my father said, he didn't want to get hit, sink,
and be chopped up, didn't want to hear
any more sailors screaming, or more of them to realize
they were about to be ground to bits by a giant propeller,
because he knew he would hear them exponentially in his sleep, forever.

But there are other forms of torment,
one my friend can tell you about at age sixty-
seven—bone spurs like tiny needles piercing his lungs,
pains in every joint and never enough medication,
abusive parents, uncaring wives, and animals mistreated.
Not to mention that perennial, universal serpent's tooth.
He can tell you about Roethke, in every anthology, a child
standing on top of a greenhouse with everybody looking up at him
(the way some of us still do), a poet loving life as much as the sailors,
the officers, the men firing torpedoes, and the men bleeding
from separate halves into the water, who loved life
more attentively than the people wanting to chop Roethke out of books.

If my friend were on watch, and a cargo of books entered his waters,
and Roethke weren't in them, he'd blow that ship out of the water,
and if the editors got chewed up by the propeller, and the publishers,
especially, he would just keep circling until they were all gone,
and those of us left would get together at the Old Folks'
Kulture Klub and hoist our beers and throw out lines
from Roethke and other dead poets about to be kicked off the page
on their way to that fate worse than death, oblivion.

Continued...

...*from previous page*

For the rest of our lives, we'd man our guns,
the birds soft-sighing above us;
our battle cry, "Snail, glister me forward!"
the barrel aimed at Academe.
The only thing is, we are getting old, *are* old,
and have not even gotten into the pages of *Poetry*
and I, at least, have few or no prospects.
In fact, we have no control over anything once we step off
the planet, a direction we are hobbling toward
faster than we like to think.
We will already have gone over the edge
when Roethke is cut loose, we hope,
so we won't have to suffer more than we're suffering now,
which is too much, just thinking about him, a great poet,
who after all is just one canary in the mine,
or, as my father would say, just one sailor in the water.

Now here we are, my friend and I,
still twenty years away from a beloved voice gone silent,
and we are already coming apart,
starting to bleed and bob and go under.
When we first stood on the greenhouse with Roethke,
which of us would've believed
the forces of darkness were already gathering;
were, in fact, trampling the flowers below, barbarians
loading their catapults with brimstone, awaiting the word?

Cathy Kodra

Bell Curve

for my mother

During the night, I dreamed you well again:
you skipped lightly down the creaking stairs,
your spine strong and straight, without a bend,
no thinning, fallen swatches of white hair.

You skipped lightly down the creaking stairs,
all smooth, efficient motion with no cane,
no thinning, fallen swatches of white hair.
You leaned upon my dream, an inclined plane.

All smooth, efficient motion with no cane,
reaching out through open porch door space,
you leaned upon my dream, an inclined plane,
and rang the copper cowbell, hanging grace.

Reaching out through open porch door space,
you shook it sharply thrice, extolling air,
rang that copper cowbell, hanging grace,
no bones calling out in grave despair.

You shook it sharply thrice, extolling air;
running through untended fields, I knew
no bones calling out in grave despair,
but cool, metallic notes called me to you.

Running through untended fields I knew
the carefully cut cheese sandwich on my plate.
Cool, metallic notes called me to you,
the spill of milk, the slice of apple cake.

The carefully cut cheese sandwich on my plate,
your eyes were clear, your voice was young and full,
the spill of milk, the slice of apple cake,
the coppery cowbell with its magic pull.

Your eyes were clear, your voice was young and full,
your spine strong and straight, without a bend,
the coppery cowbell with its magic pull:
during the night, I dreamed you well again.

'Bell Curve' appeared previously in the anthology Bleeding Hearts (Tellico Books, 2009).

Ellen LaFlèche

What My French-Canadian Grandmother
Said In Response To The Fears About
The Anthrax Postal Attacks of 2001

I'm not scared of my mailbox,
not worried, me, about no anthrax pox.

We was all afraid back then. In 1910.
The woolen mill was full of it. Didn't call
it anthrax. Wool-sorting Disease.
You was afraid to breathe,
didn't want them spores in your lungs,
in the pores of your skin.

Got that black blister on your finger,
you knew you had it. That blister could kill.
Wasn't no penicillin. No Cipro pills.

Couldn't afford no doctor then. In 1910.
You soaked your fingers in kerosene,
the best way to keep them blisters clean.
The scabs itched like hell when they healed.

You hoped your friends didn't squeal.
The bosses would fire you good. It was
understood.

We was all afraid back then. In 1910.
Wool-sorting Disease. You was afraid to breathe,
didn't want them spores in your lungs,
in the pores of your skin.

The wool was loaded with anthrax.
Them are the facts. I'm telling you, Ell,
the job was hell.

Better than working in the lumberyard, though.
You could get sliced in half,
just like that.
The worst way to go.

That happened to your Uncle Maurice, you know.

Dyeing The Child

Last week the river behind the mill ran silver,
a stream of liquid sterling.
Today the currents flow dull
yellow. Water scuds against the rocks,
a foamy scrum like potatoes boiling.

The sign says DANGER: NO SWIMMING
but Laura stands on the bank in a blue
thrift-shop bikini.

Her lover doesn't want the child
she's carrying. *Be reasonable, Laura.*
You know what you have to do.

Her belly is sleek:
only ten weeks gone. Eyes closed,
Laura jumps into the tepid dye bath.

She opens her eyes.
There is no life under this water
but her own. Her hair undulates, slow
and witchy as pond weeds.

She holds her breath,
floats past the jaundiced
limbs of a willow tree.

When she climbs out,
fingers scrabbling against the bank,
Laura's limbs shine gold in the sun.

Footprints meander across the sidewalk,
a yellow-brick path toward home.

David Krump
The Bull Moose Sum

There's an obvious balance
to which I'm oblivious: the bull moose mounted
on the lodge wall must be beautiful,
though my estimation's hindered
because I expect the rest of him—
his hind-end, torso, history—somewhere
in the next room. Imagine his winter:
large dark nostrils leaking on snow
drifting up to his odd cobbled knees.
Maybe a thin layer of ice and frost
shot across his antler tines. His tall shadow cast
remarkably sharp across a fallen oak.
And those first summer months
as a calf must have been rough;
hours at his mother's leathery teats,
with insane woodflies at his neck and eyes.
He must have longed for a lodge like this
as his first summer gave way
to first winter, then to many mature winters
spent alone in private migration
to the edible shocks on the other side. A constant
hiss as snow settled to melt on his high spine.
No companions but the occasional
drowsy owl, or the braggart squirrel
unearthing its chestnut stash, a lovely one.
Imagine him marching on and on
in the mild mercy of a storm.
Or confused in the thaw, weeks praying in runoff
for his momentary wife. His two full
balls frostbitten and heavy enough
to swing through any sturdy wall,
taking the whole damn structure down.
And in the fall, haloed by flies
in that blessed moment
spent close inside his cow
knee-deep in a cool slough
how he trembled his way
toward what it all amounts.

Katie Letcher Lyle
Love Will Take All

Love will take all your frogs
And put them in pools of water.
Having dreamed that declaration, cogs
of my sleeping brain mesh, nudging
that I ought to think about it. Now
awake in flesh I am the frogs, the pools,
the poet, puzzled, judging. Open to Dreamteller's meaning,
I take note it is oddly 2:34, think of Hubble
snapping Saturn while I dream my own
muddled dream, ribbled green, shiny and torpid
as the white Milky Way that traipses overhead.
No other guides in that stellar land of Nod.

Muzzled in sleep beside me you lie so dear
your quiet profile a deadringer for Sety One's
sere mummy we saw in Cairo, even your hands
crossed pharoahlike on your living
breathing chest, only your whispery snore
the starry certainty I need to understand
that on this febrile cloud-clad planet nothing
lasts forever but this moment, this
waking amazed to know you are here, now,
beside me by some miracle, making it clear
that *love will take all your frogs and*
and put them in pools of water.

Sarah Maté
Night Train to Memphis

Out the window another train
flashes past in the dark
fast and bright
and then it is over.

Faces without company
accept loneliness the way you settle
for less after a serious illness
and hold very still waiting.

I meet a man in the diner.
Later we throw a blanket over us
after the lights go down,
a tight fit in his sleeper
and make love to the sway
until near the town
where he gets off.
His terrier eyes are the last thing I lose.
His face blurs so fast
in snow melting on the window
that I wonder if we ever met.

In the women's lounge I find a sister
rocking her bottle of Southern Comfort
and singing "Silent Night" to her image
in the mirror. I swig the booze she shares
until I can croak in harmony with her
to the rhythm of the click-ice tracks
that coldest night when I first knew,
I wasn't going home,
I was there.

After the Circus

~ for R.W.

After the circus left her
the woman with hollow bones
and dark circles waited
tables an eye always
on the door.

She was alone like the earth
so when some traveling man
wound his way into her arms
she would dry him up.

Once a child's small, hot questions
fanned her voice. It gusted
then blew soft
about elephants
a way I never heard her voice
for any man

as if only that beast
trunk wrapped securely around her
could lift her for a moment
from this ground.

Ken McCullough's
Four Fingers and A Thumb

1. The Summer Following

The President declared a victory
then set his wooden spoon in his cracked bowl—
all that he retained except his body.
It was here he learned of his divine birth.
We drank red liquid from a waterhole
and he told us to be one with the earth.
Our days were numbered, he said, our mission
accomplished. His profile was still perfect.
We should never have crossed the Euphrates
thinking our images would not infect
the Garden of Eden and the few trees
left standing. "Subtraction and addition."
With clear eyes he told us we were home free,
the underground palace swept of debris.

2.   Hinter

The vice-president died about that time;
he had lived on a strict venom diet,
and was buoyed by a war on three fronts.
He remembered how tropical rain blunts
the libido, accept or deny it,
the taste of wild horse with a twist of lime.
His last thought was of the invisible:
One G_d, one nay shun Indy-vidual.
I used to walk with him in the foothills
and we'd sit entirely motionless.
That was before snakes whispered at my door,
after we cut off the ears of the poor.
He left us with one proviso: to bless
ourselves before we passed out the first pills.

3.   *No Honeymoon*
And here's to the Secretary of State,
hair perfect, never mussed by the wind, skate-
ing on 70,000 fathoms of
thin air. Playing an etude in the dove-
gray evening light, those fingers seek the keyboard or herself, sealed so hermetically.
Men have always taken a prurient
interest. How those sharp incisors dent
her gloves when she pulls them on with her teeth.
That she is black, just a whisper beneath
all protocol. She is alone as far
as we know; paparazzi tail her car
to no avail. If you're a WASP by birth,
male, can you ever accept her true worth?

4.   *The Harvester*
Secretary of the Interior—
to him, no one was his superior.
In a flash, he could clear cut anything,
could vaporize anything with a sting.

He had a one syllable name, like Watt,
What? Hunh? or Duh? Couldn't tell a kumquat
from a hand grenade. And RediKillo,
his Christian name; hark, the weeping willow!

But he knew board feet, he knew feet of clay.
He could harvest myriad elk per day,
he knew the count of the hairs on your head,
he had a plan for the mites in your bed.

Gone, at last, to the Cape of Commishes,
where a wind-up flounder grants his wishes.

Continued...

Marilyn McLatchey
Snow Globe

La Tour Eiffel. An April snow
      like pollen covers
            a patch of stolid tulips.

From the first platform, he leans
      over slick railings,
            leans as if in Keats' scheme

to drop and drop a red corsage
      to a woman below.
            I see it now: this is the one

of 300 steelworkers, who tumbled
      to his death clowning around.
            Her promise is to keep him

from his fall by gazing back—
      his sentinel, his figurine
            against the filmy wash of elements

against the fading colors in a dome.
      I shake it—not for snow—
            but to marvel at their hold.

... from previous page

5.   *High Command*
The general had a dogleg left on four,
popped Ritalin before noting the score.
It was a quiet day and overcast,
with a tattoo of Gandhi on his ass.
A clap of thunder silenced the blackbirds
in the oaks. In the lull, they exchanged words—
da boss and his aide-de-camp, a crew-cut:
"This next campaign will be open and shut."
This scene was mirrored in the Middle East
where a caliph was shaking down his sheik,
sank a putt in the mouth of a rough beast.
"...the price of crude and rude is on the rise,
while the price of life and pork is falling—
we must keep our veiléd eyes on the prize."

Veronica Patterson
Dead End Job

It's March. The man picking debris from the gutters, puddles, scars of snow, wears a stocking cap and flannel shirt, its sleeves washed short. His spiked pole pierces every scrap and cup; he scrapes the paper kabob into his black plastic bag. Tonight, he will sit in a 40-watt circle of light, smooth each crumpled possibility, bend to it. You might think of this as a dead end job. Sometimes he dreams of indoor work and benefits. Yet one note says, "Meet me tonight. You know where," but he doesn't. So he walks toward the full moon's breathless orange as it rises to distant silver. He sits on a sliver of rocky island dividing a stream that sings *meltwater*. He read once that any scrap might hold the secret name of God. And it's March, windy, he knows all the long fences, the wires and barbs that will snag and tear everything he doesn't rescue.

Q: Why Did Spring Invent Impressionism?

A: because one cottonwood loosed from cunning packets ten thousand tufted dreams the wind puzzled over fruit trees disguised in April snow dislodging petals to whirl with sticky pinwheels into grass combed by giddy concerts of light conducting birds into nests whistling binding beguiling wheedling see see me in the churn and turn of air-mapped perfumes—of course there was still death in Rembrandt darks with one stroke of light from saints tortured somewhere, but the brush!—every hair dizzied by the hum of daub splatter drum pointing there there there though it could have been winter, a railroad station, one blue street where dusk lingered in tendrils

Suzanne Owens

Music on the Magnetic
River of Let's Return

Tutto Tutto: all, whole
Molto: much, more
Presto: quickly
Da Capo: repeat from the beginning

Two notes lean on the bar
in double time.
Her treble trembles a little.
His base rises as he moves
into her space.
She believes his line,
gives him a
grace-note look with her eyes.
No blues in their talk.
First a little syncopation, then
it's all jazz and riff—

Tutto. Tutto.

When the tempo is right,
she answers with
a trill to his staccato suggestion,
why don't we walk by the river,
so they drift legato into a duet,
finally sit on a ledger line by the
water,
each a Serenade
anticipating
Chamber Music . . .

Molto. Molto.

Some foreplay--in harmony
until a minor kiss
turns major.
Then, *rubato*
while he plays nocturne piano
on her *tit-*
ivating changes of key.

She's diminuendo until
a flat,
a sharp
and their Sonata begins
for-tissimo . . .
They strum and pick,

Presto. Presto.

an exercise for all five fingers flowing
as the river flows,
a liquid mastery with mouths,
and from the long grasses
their bodies
arpeggio, jump octaves, crescendo...
No cadence,
no rests. They are
Samba, Soul, Muse. They're wings.
They are
a Symphony.

Da Capo. Da Capo.

JoAnne Preiser
On the Set

They're making a movie
at the old state mental institution;
they're making it look
like it's 1954
like it's an island
off the coast of Boston.

They're making hurricanes blow
with an aircraft engine
and rain pour at an angle
that tears at a wall of windows
canted just enough
to prevent the camera's reflection.

They're making *the talent*
scale a cliff
made of medium
density fiberboard,
MDF in the trade,
rock that rises
all of six feet
from the ground.

In the woods
behind the cottage
that once housed
sex offenders,
they built a cemetery
and a mausoleum
with stones
that look like New England
granite but weigh less
than your shoe.
Even the felled trees
are fake—pipes
covered with more MDF,
thin sheets of rubber
molded like bark.

They're flying in rats
from LA
to follow a whistle
and two alpha males.
They'll peek out
of their MDF cave
for a close-up
then jump
to a long shot
on prefabricated ground
cut
to the water's edge
which is not
the rocky coast of Maine,
not even the sandy shore
of Carson's Beach,
but a tank
with two hydraulic pumps
shooting out water
every six seconds
and sucking it back
till they're ready for more.

A world all its own
where night reigns
as the sun beats down
and daylight lasts
long after the moon
rises over the real
cemetery farther down
Hospital Road
where 839 inmates
lie buried, their nameless
plots marked
by small stones
etched with numbers
to credit their lives.

'On The Set' previously appeared in Literal Latte, online.

Jonathan Rice
After Perseids

The last time we tried for a child, what we started
was gone before the moon went dark

over August. It'd been two weeks since she bent double
in pain, and we were lost after midnight, with ocean

on either sides of the dunes, and nearly out of fuel.
I knew we would be stranded for the night

and unable to sleep with the stars bearing down
on our faces. Then the meteors broke from Perseus,

and I thought that the world might be ending,
so stopped the car to look on in indignation

and awe. Light fell in streaks above us, then near
the horizon, beneath the curve to open sea.

And we were alone again, with the wash of sand
across the road like the furl of a bedsheet.

*

A year ago, that night on the Outer Banks,
and the shadowing grief still holds certain days.

The half month she'd have been born passed
unmentioned into New Year's without resolution,

then Easter, with no return to trying again.
And I am thinking of my grandfather, who wanted

to write the arc of his life before he was too sick
to do so. In the front pages, before the sections

dedicated to his sons, and before Korean fields
of teenage soldiers wearing new sneakers

and the flamethrower wielded over the killed
and living alike, is a spate of blank pages, with a line

leading off at the start, proving my fear that the burden
of loss skips generations: *for Sarah, who was not born.*

*

That night we found the one gas station still open.

The attendant blinked dully under her halogen veil
to take my money, looking up only to count the bills.

And then we were silent and driving towards a hotel
of dark rooms and skeleton staff, and slowed to read

historical markers, one telling us we were near
where the first child born of English settlers, a girl,

disappeared with the rest of the colony. Half a word
carved into a tree, and nothing else remained. Then it was

too easy to watch for her, or the ghost of her crouching
in the sawgrass or running the length of a forgotten game

across the mantles of dunes, and to believe
the lone streetlight far ahead, when the sea broke into view,

was a cairn still burning for ships that would not come.

'After Perseids,' a finalist for the 2007 Wabash Poetry Prize, previously appeared in Sycamore Review, Vol. 20, Issue 1, Winter 2008.

Barbara Smith-Alfaro
Oddly American

In McDonald's this afternoon a punch
drunk fighter with a squashed face
shared a table with a woman
perhaps in her late fifties.
She was wearing button earrings,
a white blouse, blue skirt,
perfectly polished shoes,
her Lord &Taylor shopping bag
nestled beside her with its single rose.
The fighter wore dark clothes,
and spoke constantly.
His voice sounded scraped, raw,
and it was difficult for me
to listen to him without wincing.

Sometimes the woman looked away
but only for a moment, then
rested her chin on her joined hands
and leaned forward toward him
the way listening women do.
She looked like actresses
in old movies, ladylike,
lovely, and oddly American.
The fighter's face had been hurt
so often and so brutally
he no longer resembled himself.
Perhaps once he looked like Vinnie Love,
a boxer I knew when I was sixteen,
his face so beautiful I couldn't believe
he wanted to be a fighter.

Vinnie took me to a party.
Most of the people were drunk.
An older man, a writer,
beckoned me to join him
in another room. I followed him.
The light was turned out.

He slid his hands along my legs.
The door opened. Vinnie switched
on the light and began
punching the writer.
Later, voices, and the writer asking
that the light be turned off. And while
the fighter in McDonald's is talking,
at another table a baby
is mangling a handful of French fries.

I'm remembering my dress,
at home—so much blood
I threw it away. When
Vinnie called in the morning,
I didn't want to talk,
didn't want to hear his voice.
I spoke but only pretended to listen.

Today I'm thinking of how
the angels fought. They had no wings
but moved as quickly as thought.
They never used their hands
but stunned and kept enemies from them
with sound, the way whales do.
In other occasions, they playfully made
garlands of breath-whispers humans
could not see but felt brushing tenderly.

What did his voice sound like
before it was wounded—liquid, sure?
Did he have a New York accent
or sound vaguely foreign
as sons of immigrants sometimes do?
Which pounding caused what would never heal?

The woman from Lord & Taylor
did not reach over and touch
the fighter's hand but I wanted her to.

'Oddly American' previously appeared in Poet Lore, Vol.4, # 2.

Laura Still
Dance of the Manatees

The *ballible* began in the dark, sibilant exhalations,
mysterious splish-sploshings, soft bumps swaying the boat,
an awareness of larger bodies surrounding us, invisible beings
assembling as inky water reflected the starry night.
Dawn brought huge gray-green shapes looming up to mist the surface
with their breath, *en avant* and *arriere,* in groups of two or three.
In your wetsuit and snorkel you glided easily into the circling dance;
a curious *danseuse* nuzzled your mask, gazed soulfully into your eyes,
executing a *demi detourne* to allow you to stroke her belly.
My partner ducked his head, hung back till I coughed,
a *glissade* brought him to my side, his drooping eyes black, soft,
shy but solicitous. I touched his back, slick with algae,
skin grainy and firm beneath. We floated inches apart; my fingers
found livid white scars raking his sides—wounds from propellers.
He blinked sweetly and I stroked him, ashamed of my species,
till cold caused my hand to shake, signaling the *coda.*
He swam with me to the boat, a courteous *danseur* relinquishing
his ballerina after a *pas de deux*, before rejoining the ring
revolving around us, submarine *adagio* waltz
wrapping us in wonder while overhead in *grand jete*
a rainbow blessed our morning.

I See Rainbows

In rings around the sun on hazy mornings,
misty evenings; a stained glass window
flashes where the cloud thins to a veil.
Jeweled spirals reflect in glass pebbles,
prisms flutter at the edge of candle flames,
even street signs iridesce in the dawn.

I see rainbows
no one else sees, for my vision altered
when I passed through the spectrum,
pieces of multi-hued arc imprinted
my brain, an invisible kaleidoscope
spinning and changing all around me.
The fornix inside me signals the light:
bend, divide, and colors reveal themselves.

I see rainbows
for light begets light, grows within my body
till it bubbles and tingles beneath my skin,
surrounds me with prisms leaked from eyes,
ears, mouth, ends of my hair sparking
with escaped energy, links me to the chain
of light that unites all eternity. Translated,

I will be rainbows.

Joseph A. Soldati
Rain in Murano

The day begins with a white-hooded
cappuccino—celebrant of mornings—
and a dense hunk of *pane pescatore*
that I break and dip into the sweet
cumulus atop the black hole of coffee.

What rain? though it falls like the tropes
of unlucky poets not in Italy this spring,
those who will not be joining me to drink
a bottle of crisp *Soave* or to dine
on *Sarde in saor* and *Farfelle* with salmon.

I can barely see Venice across the lagoon,
and the footbridges that cross the canals
of this little town are slick, my steps
cautious (I could fall and break something)
here on Italy's glass isle.

Too wet for my notebook and pen
in the piazza, and with no desire
to seek the lee side and read Virgil
in my room, I wander brilliant
galleries of *vitro di trina* so fragile

that a breath might shatter it all,
then visit the *fornace* to watch
a *soffiatore* hold a dazzling nova
on his pipe before he blows
the white-hot star into a warm sun.

Michael Sweeney
Patriots Now

Copacetic since Valley Forge & talk about playing hurt! nobody
would've broken ranks if redcoats bullrushed the camp—we'd be
fixing our bayonets with frostbitten blackened stumps. Baron von
Steuben drove us like serfs over that foetid ground, cursed our
mothers in German & French till nobody felt abashed by the blitz-
krieg & subterfuge. Bob Kraft said it at XXXVI, we're all of us
Patriots now. Soon we'd all reload so fast we got off two volleys
to one, Tedy Bruschi shook off his stroke & we could nail close-
order drill like typhus & bloody flux never unloosened our guts.
Soon enough we'd march northeast to Monmouth & points beyond
to bludgeon each dastardly musketeer down in a three-point stance,
we don't want no headlong rout, we want their greasy scalps, we
want to blast them to smithereens from Indy to al-Anbar, down
the Mississippi close to New Orleans via the Trail of Tears, we
want to pry their facemasks off & gouge their offending eyes,
shame their prophet at Abu Ghraib & starve 'em at Andersonville,
we want to discombobulate the gray matter coiled in their skulls,
ram our helmets into their sternum & sever the spinal cord, we
want to rip their testes out & swallow 'em while they're hot! Just
admit you roared when we left them prone on the ten-yard line,
spastic as flounder in our wake gasping that Foxboro air; please
concede you begged us to drag them by their disgraceful braids
& dump their ungodly corpse outside the Meadowlands to rot
in the Jersey sun—all we heard was surge & despoil, sack &
eradicate since hashmarks were drawn & worn, from Canton
to San Juan Hill. And don't blow taps when we're slain at last,
sprawled on synthetic grass under a neutral dome—Hog Hannah's
still aggrieved that Tatum put Stingley down & we're all of us
Patriots now

Pamela Spiro Wagner
Three, For Those Left Behind

1. *Grieving and Staying*

The dead do not need us
to grieve or tear our hair
or keen extravagantly.
Stepping free of flesh
a double exposure (one ghost
rising from bed, another napping
at mid-day), their spirits follow
the curves of their late bodies,
rehearsing again and again
what we're always too late for.
Just so, my friend Susie,
scrubbed clean of life's debris,
twenty years later returning
in my dream of the dead
returning and I can't let go
my guilty retrospection,
the arrogant suspicion
I could have saved her.
Now, though I know no dream
will return her utterly, I cling
to this one: Susie and I at twenty-one
standing before two doors,
how she points me towards the one
where a celebration is taking place
then disappears through the other
marked No Exit, as if it has to be,
as if it's fair, as if either
of us in this world
has ever had a choice.

2. *At the Lake, Under the Moon*

In memory, the moon's always a new dime,
glinting off the dark chop, ticking the night away

ruthless and indifferent as a parking meter.
As always, the lake shimmers, ebony splashed

with silver and we're sitting there at the end
of the dock, thirteen, dangling our bare feet

above the water's coruscating skin. We barely
ruffle the surface but it's enough

to shatter the still shaft of moonglow,
potsherds of mercury, dancing tesserae, a mosaic

of light illuminating the water.
Is it possible we don't yet suspect

how things must turn out? We shed our clothes
to swim shy and bare-skinned, silvered bubbles

rising to the surface like stars
of the wayward constellations

by which we'll navigate our separate lives.
What we know is this: the sleek water

rolling off our skin, the frangible sand, schools of
glowing nightfish nosing amid algae.

We can't guess how fate will interpose
its coups and tragedies, how far in ten years

we will have traveled from that night.
I never got to say good-bye.

I scatter your white ashes,
moonlight over dark water.

3. *In My Dreams You Are Not Silent*

Time heals nothing
but the space left behind
is filled, little by little,
with the critical minutiae
that make a life: shirts
at the cleaners, supper
in its pots, a half-read book
overdue at the library,
lying open, face down,
on the table.

*'Three, For Those Left Behind'
previously appeared in a different form and with a different
title in the Tunxis Review. It
also appears in Wagner's book,
We Mad Climb Shaky Ladders
(2009, CavanKerry Press, Fort
Lee, NJ).*

SIAM

Contemplation

poems that
come unannounced
i let go free.
instead—i
am captured by them
on invisible parchment—be
yond the realm of pub
lication or pri
vate readings.

I—
like the wind still search for definition—the
approval i thought i once
needed is now gently wrapped
in the mantle of self acceptance
& worn by beings who live
on a humorous planet where there
is no need for dialogue—or
applause.

Plumage

for Allyson

watch,
i will do it
once for you, &
it will be real,

i will open
my plumage &
expose my colors to
your beholding,

for a moment in time
i will stand & radiate
my essence to you,
for you,
through you,
&
into you,

be
sure
to
wear
your
sun
glasses.

Candance Reaves
Come Back

Come back before the
sheets begin to cool,
my lips cease to swell and sting,
my breasts forget your tongue,
my back the path of a bead of sweat, or
your hand defining its arch.

Come back before the walls forget the
sounds of our breathing, the
low growl of your animal
rising to the throat,
my heart's tympanic thrum.

Come back before the scent of the ocean and
all it contains,
the small perfumes of our bodies
dissipate or
my vision dims with the darkness
as it penetrates the window,
and the memory
of the blueness of your eyes
goes gray.

Anthony Russell White
The Girl with Extra Electricity

She wore a copper bracelet on her left ankle. Simple. 1/8" round in cross-section. It bounced as she walked, and trailed a six-inch copper wire, mostly sheathed in black plastic, but exposed and frayed at one end. The other end was expertly soldered to and through a hole in the ring. Neatly buffed so as not to scratch her pale skin. She said it kept her grounded. Bled off the excess electricity to which her body was so prone. Wore it always, she said. Even three years ago, when she was a bridesmaid for her oldest childhood friend. Caused raised eyebrows from the bride's snooty mother and her friends. A grad student in the engineering lab had helped her make it, exactly to the specifications in her dream. She never saw him again, but is convinced he will be there at the lab in Toledo if she ever needs a new wire. Or it gets mangled in a bicycle accident and has to be replaced. She said it worked even better after she got the tattoos. Twin lightning bolts, from the men's catalog at the Skull and Rose Unisex Tattoos and Piercings. One on either side of the ankle, above the copper ring. Right where it hurts the most, they warned her. But well worth the pain. When she left the train at noon in Piacenza, and descended the three aluminum steps to the platform, the wire skipped behind her. And when it hit the puddle below on the asphalt, there was a tiny spark. And another when she turned into the ladies' toilet, as the wire swung out beside her like the tail of a miniature comet and brushed the metal post holding up the roof.

'The Girl with Extra Electricity' previously appeared in e: Emily Dickinson Anthology (2000), Caesura 25th Anniversary issue (2004), and White's chapbook, Ferrovie (Červená Barva Press, 2007).

Diana Woodcock
Choosing A Desert

When you decide the time has come
for a move to the desert, consider this one:
peninsula with Arabian Gulf waters on three
sides, an inland sea, flamingos in the shallows,
songs of that Persian nightingale—the white-
cheeked bulbul—pure magical

incantations, the sidra tree spreading its
branches like arms raised in praise.
In the silence and solitude, you'll learn to
love your neighbor for who he is—not
what he claims to be. In this harsh place,
you'll find within yourself the grace of

gentleness. Sea lavender will draw you to
saline flats you might otherwise avoid,
moorhen and crakes to sewage lagoons hidden
by tall green reeds. You'll grow so accustomed
to arid flat tan terrain till you'll feel like an alien
in lush mountains and rain. You'll settle in,

but once in a while the cloud-moving wind will
stir the chords of vagabondage, and you'll long
for a mountain stream and the woodsong.
You'll thirst for rain—day-long rain, rain that
drenches your dreams all night. You'll miss birches
and mushrooms. But there's a seamlessness in all this

barrenness—a sand-brown transience that shouldn't
be missed: quiet inlets with gentle ripples, springtime
with desert hyacinths blossoming, the season of
mists when the desert scrub drips with moisture.
This is the place to enter the cloister of your own
design—take all the time you need to simply be.

*'Choosing a Desert' previously appeared in Quercus Review, April/
May 2007 & Creekwalker, Summer 2007.*

Alexandra Wild
The Irrational

When there is news
of the coming of the end of the world
and every family is huddled together waiting
and the offices have been abandoned
and the cattle in the dairy farms turned free,
there will be a few fools left
diligently doing their work
with total disregard for common sense
somehow believing that there is still a cause
worth living for.

Perhaps unable to stop,
they will question their apparent idiocy
as their hands and voices and pens continue
uninterrupted, with or without their will:
they will believe with the faith
only possible in the mad or the dying.
They will tell themselves
this creation will transcend
not only time but also
the ruin of earth and humanity.

Perhaps five minutes before the end
when every person is holding the hands of another
or taking drugs or praying
and the cattle become anxious
they will continue with urgency more than before
to capture this essential moment
imagining that somewhere in the universe
the echoes of their work will be heard.
What Death's prospect cannot stop:
this becomes the focal trance
of the last viewing of life.

In this dream witness
the making of a nuclear explosion

Continued...

Robert Carl Williams
I Met the Hour On The Road

We paused as intimates, now bent
like boughs of hemlocks laden
with snow, acknowledging

the years we spent growing old
as the evening deepened in blue around us,
chicory along the roadsides we traveled

alone and together,
each lifetime becoming
more beautiful,

like the hickory handle of Daddy's ax worn
by the calluses of his hand. We stood
in silence for a hundred years, tasting

the tart of age, oak of the barrel, after
frost had sweetened the apple,
all the words having been lavished,

fallen leaves of September.

that would robe the earth in red silk
and rub away any possible traces of life;
find it significant.
Follow the foggy irrationality of the dream person
taking pens that will melt
paper that will be burned into dust
and the words that will refuse to evaporate.
With the regretful wind came
a hushed whish
of a yellow flame.

Lansing King
Piper

Boy, you'd let it run full on out but scared
and keep speed up / nose down,
throttle up in simple craft of fear
you'd hit the tops of the trees and
sometimes just the wheels would
graze and that was over soon and on the
breeze, worth it for the chance you'd take.

Then clear and climbing like Amelia climbing on a
good day, Amelia dancing on a good day on the wind,
aloft and free of fear-cares of ground, unfettered,
goose flying back North. *You Goose, I love you, Goose*
she'd say.

Over back and back to compass South and
dancing frail in gusts, a surrender
to the gusts, light and frail.
Glass and skating now

Doors—canvas on warped old hardwood frames see
through crack, a view to hold the ant hill world below
and pattern it to understanding. A fragile older airplane.

You'd see the rims of range and rays spewing
over the range, push nose down maintain then
up up on big God Hand thermal from the south and sunny side.

Sky-King-Penny-Ponytail-Flying down to Memphis now
into the going-down sun like Sun Records and Elvis sacred
singing to Colonel Tom to see'f he'd take him on and sign him.

And wonder it might be dark when you got there and if
you'd see to land and then see to see her.

But wait too there's fear of getting close when I get you close
there, close to you and how you've changed since I saw you
last and know you'd never stand a *change* with me or was it me with you?

Wheels on landing barely graze the tops of trees,
a sumi brush of bamboo leaves in silence, painting?

Prozac

1. Then

A woman I know took Prozac for a year.

She compared the advantages, disadvantages,
of taking the drug to even her moods, keep herself level,
to keep her sweet feet on solid ground.

Said on it she could appreciate
the value of comfortable shoes,
a bowl of soup at night but sometimes missed
her heart transported towards simple ecstasy
by light off wet yellow leaves in fall.

2. Now

A friend said of me,
Watch! If you let him,
he will steer you toward things.

Yet times, midst all the confusion,
all the chaos,
round a corner, I'll see
a breakthrough of clarity and truth.
(I think)
and want to share with all I know and like,
and some I don't;
ideas, waves of light, inklings of God.

Comes with a price and a grace
like a dance you can do.

~ Notes On Contributors ~

Frances Payne Adler is the author of *Making of a Matriot* (Red Hen Press), *Raising The Tents* (Calyx Books), both poetry, and three collaborative poetry-photo books. She founded Creative Writing and Social Action Program at CSU, Monterey Bay. Her newest book, co-edited with Diana Garcia and Debra Busman, is *Fire and Ink: An Anthology of Social Action Writing* (University of Arizona Press).

Allison Alsup and husband moved from San Francisco to New Orleans eight years ago, where they renovated a 100-year-old cottage. The former teacher is renovating a second house, the lot next door, and annoying the neighbors with her drumming.

Anita M. Barnard, a Fort Worth poet and artist, has co-edited four poetry anthologies, most recently *Above Us Only Sky, Vol. 2* (Incarnate Muse Press) and edited the anthology *Sense of Touch*. Poems have appeared in *Comstock Review, Illya's Honey, Borderlands*, and the *2008 Texas Poetry Calendar*. She's been a finalist for *NMW* and Muriel Craft Bailey awards and nominated for a Pushcart Prize.

Rhonda Bear is a former photojournalist who teaches Spanish, English and Citizenship classes in her own center. She gardens and enjoys visits from her three children, a grandson and lots of birds. She writes essays and poems.

Ellen Bihler is a registered nurse working in long term pediatric care. Her poetry has appeared in *Cream City Review, American Journal of Nursing, Square Lake, International Poetry Review* and elsewhere. She is the author of the chapbooks, *Late Summer Confessions* (Pudding House, '09) and *An Avalanche of Blue Sky* (Foothills, '04). She and her husband live in Hackettstown, NJ.

Christine E. Black's work has appeared or is forthcoming in *Aura Literary Arts Review, Antietam Review, 13th Moon, Margie, NMW, Nimrod, Red Rock Review* and other publications. Honors include a Pushcart nomination. She lives in Charlottesville, VA, with her husband, artist John P. Black, and two young sons.

Deborah Brown is an editor of *Lofty Dogmas: Poets on Poetics* (University of Arkansas, 2005) and co-translator of *The Last Voyage: The Poems of Giovanni Pascoli* (Red Hen Press). Poems have appeared in *Margie, Rattle, Alaska Quarterly* and other journals. She teaches writing and literature at University of New Hampshire-Manchester and lives in Warner with her husband and four cats.

Madelyn Camrud is the author of *This House Is Filled With Cracks* (New Rivers Press, 1994) and a chapbook, *The Light We Go After* (Dacotah Territory Press, 2007). An Associate Poet Laureate of North Dakota, she retired in 2001 from a decade of work at North Dakota Museum of Art. She lost her husband of 51 years in June, 2008. She is working on a related book about Alzheimer's and Parkinson's diseases.

E.R. Carlin grew up in Youngstown, OH, and has an MFA from Pacific Lutheran. He has worked in restaurants, construction, 3D hologram sales, as a teacher's assistant, peace activist, "and now as a union-less lecturer at Cazenovia College in New York." His work has appeared in *Beloit Poetry Journal, Cimarron Review, Hiram Poetry Review, Hunger, Minnesota Review, New South, Poems & Plays, Rattle* and others.

Marianne Chrystalbridge "lives by mountains and seas wherever she finds them, and has three daughters on whom the sun rises and sets." She teaches courses on geography and power at Pellissippi State Community College and is a former member of Knoxville's memorable 1998 Poetry Slam Team.

Deborah DeNicola is the author of *Inside Light,* a chapbook from Finishing Line Press and spiritual memoir *The Future That Brought Her Here* (Nicholas Hays/Ibis Press, 2009). A full collection of poetry, *Original Human,* is scheduled for 2010 from Custom Words Press. She edited *Orpheus & Company, Contemporary Poems on Greek Mythology* (University Press of New England). Previous books include *Where Divinity*

Begins (Alice James Books) and prize-winning chapbooks. She received an NEA in 1997. She reviews poetry for *The Fort Lauderdale Sun-Sentinel* and works as a mentor and dream guide at www.intuitivegateways.com.

Rusty Dolleman is a former Wallace Stegner Fellow in Fiction at Stanford University, and a graduate of University of New Hampshire's writing program.

Gary Thomas Edwards "was born a hippie. Today, although I dress a bit more conservatively… my heart still beats in 1968…. An eclectic tapestry of memories and influences combine to make me who I am."

Stephanie Elliott is the recipient of an Academy of American Poets Prize for her poem, *What the Tattoo Artist Said,* herein. Her poems have appeared in *Lewis and Clark Literary Review, Imagination and Place,* an anthology, and *Jefferson Monthly.* She lives in Oakland, CA, where she is employed by *Mad Science* as "a paper airplane engineer and a card-house architect." She also practices yoga and grows tomatoes.

Renee Epling "lives in a purple Victorian with Bimmer, a GSD/wolf rescue, a Fila Brasileiro named Kharma, and Tallulah, the American Pitbull Terrier."

Steve Fayer won a national Emmy for his work on the PBS series, *Eyes On The Prize,* and a Writers' Guild of America Award for *George Wallace: Settin' The Woods On Fire.* He is co-author of *Voices of Freedom,* a history of the Civil Rights Movement" (Bantam, 1990). His fiction has appeared in *Bellevue Literary Review, Dos Passos Review, Natural Bridge, New York Stories* and elsewhere.

Ed Frankel teaches for the UCLA Writing Programs and Antioch Los Angeles BA and MFA programs. Nominated for a Pushcart, he has won first prizes from *Confluence,* Winning Writers War Poetry and *New American Review* chapbook contests. His chapbook, *When the Catfish Are In Bloom: Requiem for John Fahey,* was recently nominated for a PEN Award and California Book Award. His latest chapbook is *People Of The Air* (2009). His website is www.Edfrankel.com.

Carol Gilbertson's poems appeared most recently in *Christian Century, Flyway, Jefferson Monthly* and *The MacGuffin.* Awards include *Flyway's* Sweet Corn Poetry Prize and Donald Murray Prize for essay. She co-edited *Translucence: Religion, the Arts and Imagination* (Fortress, 2004), and teaches at Luther College in Decorah, IA.

Melanie Hoffert has an MFA from Hamline University where her manuscript, *The Silent Land...* was selected for the 2008 Outstanding Creative Nonfiction Award. She also won *Baltimore Review's* Creative Nonfiction Award. Her work has appeared in *Muse & Stone* and *The Mochila Review.*

Don Hynes, husband, father, and grandfather, a Notre Dame honors graduate, lives and writes in his adopted hometown of Portland, OR. Author of three volumes of poetry, *Slender Arrow* (1998), *Out from Under* (2001) and *The Living Dark* (2007) (www.donhynes.com) as well as the monthly online political commentary *Vantage Point* (www.vpdonhynes.blogspot.com), Don is a tradesman, builder, and large projects construction manager and owner's rep. www.cpmdonhynes.com.

Katharine Goodridge Ingram was born in Mexico to US parents. She lived on Avenida Malintzin (or Malinche), named for Cortés' interpreter. Her work has appeared in *A Tribute to Ray Bradbury, Café Solo, Santa Barbara Review* and in *Community of Voices* anthologies. She has completed a Mexico memoir, story and poetry collections, and is at work on a novel set in Michoacán, Mexico.

Doris Ivie, "retired head of college English, then psychology programs, is resting on her laurels in her treehouse, attending spiritual retreats and book groups, and celebrating life—with infinite gratitude."

Trish Lindsey Jaggers' poems have appeared in *The Louisville Review, Briar Cliff Review, Round Table, Matter 11: The Woods, Red Rock Review, Clackamas Literary Review, Heartland Review, Blue Moon Rising: Kentucky Women in Transition, Tobacco Anthology* and elsewhere. She assists the director of Women's Studies at Western Kentucky University and teaches at WKU's community college. She has an MFA in creative writing from Spalding University.

Leland James is the author of college texts, two novels and a book of essays. He has published in academic and popular periodicals, including *Galaxy Science Fiction, Journal of Rehabilitation Medicine* and *Production Engineering*. His poetry has won awards and has appeared in *Inspirit, Portland Pen, Ruminate, By Line, Harûah, Voices of Israel* and *Cyclamens and Swords*.

Tim Johnson, a software engineer since 1982, "has always had a penchant for creative writing on the side. The kids are grown and the writing bug has re-emerged!"

Marilyn Kallet is the author of 14 books, including *Packing Light: New and Selected Poems* (Black Widow Press, 2009). She is Lindsay Young Professor of English at the University of Tennessee, where she directed creative writing for 17 years. She teaches poetry for the Virginia Center for Creative Arts in Auvillar, FR.

Pat Landreth Keller of Middle Georgia is a former recipient of a Georgia Arts Council award. A poetry chapbook, *Draglines*, was selected for the Toadlily Press Quartet series. *An Uncommon Accord* debuted in November, 2009. Poems have appeared or are forthcoming in *MCV, The Pinch, Caesura* and *Healing Muse*.

Lansing King is a Knoxville, TN, architect. His first published poems appear herein. "Goodbye little poems. Have a safe journey and call home if you get work."

Cathy Kodra, native New Yorker, lives, writes, and edits in Knoxville, TN. Her poems, essays, and short stories have appeared or will appear in *Tar Wolf Review, Main Channel Voices, NMW, Outscape: Writings on Fences and Frontiers, Birmingham Arts Journal, Roanoke Review, Common Ground Review* and others.

David Krump's works have appeared in *Colorado Review, Greensboro Review, Poetry, Poetry Review* (UK) and *Verse*. Honors include a Ruth Lilly Fellowship, Lorine Niedecker Award and the 2008 Poetry Foundation/Newberry Library Fellowship. Poetry editor of *Oranges & Sardines,* a review, he earned a masters with distinction from Oxford and teaches composition and poetry at Viterbo University. His new chapbook is *From the Guidebook to the End of the World* (TAIGA Press).

Ellen LaFlèche has published poetry in *Alehouse, Alligator Juniper, The Ledge, Skidrow Penthouse, Naugatuck River Review,* among others. She recently won second prize in the Paradise Poetry Contest for her poem celebrating Jacoby Ellsbury, first Navajo to play major league baseball. She works in Western Massachusetts as an editor specializing in academic writing.

Eric Lester is a computer network director. Read his works at www.eflester.com.

Judith Ann Levison lives in New Hope, PA.

Ellaraine Lockie has authored five chapbooks and received 11 Pushcart nominations and honors from *The Eleventh Muse*, Writecorner Press, Skysaje Poetry, the Dean Wagner and Elizabeth R. Curry prizes. Recently released are *Mod Gods and Luggage Straps*, a poetry/art broadside from BrickBat Revue and *Blue Ribbons at the County Fair* (PWJ), a chapbook of award winners. "Coming Home in a Haibun" won the Illinois Poetry Society Formal Poetry award.

Peter Lopatin, after practicing commercial and corporate law for 28 years, became a teacher of English as a Second Language and now teaches at the University of

Connecticut/Stamford. He is also managing editor of WebVet.com, concerning pets. He's been published in *Poetry East* and his first published story, *"Nathan at the Speed of Light,"* was in the October 2009 issue of *Commentary.*

Naomi Ruth Lowinsky, a Jungian analyst, "keeps company with ghosts. They show up in her poems, and several, including Sappho, have a lot to say in her forthcoming memoir, *The Sister from Below: When the Muse Gets Her Way.* She is widely published, recently in *Runes, Texas Review* and *Weber Studies.*

Katie Letcher Lyle of Lexington, VA, is the author of 16 books and many articles. Her fiction has appeared in *Viva, Shendandoah,* and *Virginia Quarterly.* A writer, teacher and folksinger, she taught 25 years at Southern Seminary College, and has taught at Hollins University, Washington and Lee, Mary Baldwin College, and Randolph-Macon Woman's College. She has taught over 250 Elderhostels. She has two grown children. Active in organizations that serve the handicapped, she serves on the Rockbridge Area Hospice Board. To order books, Google, or visit *www.katieletcherlyle.com.*

Sarah Maté has been published in *Poet Lore, The Devil's Millhopper, NMW* and elsewhere. A retired English teacher from Maryland, she lives in Maryville, TN, where she volunteers to help the hungry. She likes hanging out with her dog Buster.

Marilyn McLatchey, a humanities professor at Valencia Community College at Winter Park, FL, has been published in the *American Poetry Journal* and *National Poetry Review* and many others. Awards include the Annie Finch poetry prize.

Ken McCullough's most recent books of poetry are *Obsidian Point* (2003) and *Walking Backwards* (2005) as well as a book of stories, *Left Hand* (2004). Honors include an Academy of American Poets award, NEA Fellowship, Pablo Neruda and Galway Kinnell awards, *NMW*, Blue Light Book and Capricorn awards, a Jerome Foundation grant (to continue translating the work of U Sam Oeur, survivor of the Pol Pot regime in Cambodia). Books written with U include *Sacred Vows*, a bilingual edition of U's poetry (1998) and U's *Crossing Three Wildernesses* (2005). McCullough lives in Winona, MN, with his wife and younger son. An administrator at Saint Mary's, UM, he teaches at Hawk's Well Literary Center.

Sarah Miller lives in Somerville, MA, in a small loft with her husband Jim and dog, Maggie. "I'm madly in love with my job working as Dean of Student and Family Support at Phoenix Charter Academy in Chelsea, MA. Raised in East Tennessee, I spend a lot of daydreams missing the south."

RB Morris, poet, singer, songwriter, musician, playwright and actor, hails from Knoxville, TN. His poetry books include *Early Fires, Littoral Zone,* and *The Man Upstairs.* He wrote and acted in *The Man Who Lives Here Is Loony*, a one-man play taken from the life and work of James Agee. His musical recordings include *Take That Ride, Zeke and the Wheel, Empire,* and the soon to be released *Spies, Lies, and Burning Eyes.* Morris served as Jack E. Reese Writer-in-Residence at UT 2004-08.

Barack Hussein Obama, U.S. President, authored *Dreams of My Father, The Audacity of Hope* and a number of poems, speeches, essays and other writings.

Suzanne Owens received her MFA from Emerson College, Boston, MA. She is the author of *The Daughters Of Discorda* (BOA Editions), winner of the A. Poulin Jr., New Poet's of America series, 2000. A graduate of the American Musical and Dramatic Academy, NYC, she attended the Guildhall of Music and Drama, London ENG. She won The Frank Cat Press Chapbook Award, 1996, for *Theater Poems.* Others include *In The Lake's Eye* and *Harvesting Ice* (Finishing Line Press) and *Over The Edge* (Pudding House Press).

Veronica Patterson is a graduate of Cornell, University of Michigan, University of Northern Colorado, and the Warren Wilson College MFA program. Her poetry books include *How to Make a Terrarium* (Cleveland State University, 1987), *Swan, What Shores?* (NYU Press, 2000) and *Thresh & Hold* (2009) winner of the Gell Poetry Prize. Her poems have appeared in *Malahat Review, Another Chicago Magazine, Cimarron Review, New Letters, Prairie Schooner, Southern Poetry Review,* and *Spoon River.*

Dannye Romine Powell, news columnist for the *Charlotte Observer* is the author of *A Necklace of Bees,* winner of the Brockman-Campbell Poetry Award. She also won fellowships from the NEA and North Carolina Arts Council.

JoAnne Preiser writes and teaches in Massachusetts. As a member of Fine Line Poets (www.finelinepoets.com.) she has conducted writing workshops in the Boston area. Her poems have appeared or are forthcoming in *Alehouse Press, Memoir* and *Slipstream.* Poems have been honored in *The Ledge, Inkwell* and by *Literal Latté* online. Her first chapbook is *Confirmation* (Finishing Line Press).

Aliene Pylant's poetry has appeared in *Raintown Review, Texas Poetry Calendar* and *The Formalist.* Her poem, "Unerring Mercy and Pure Grace," won the 2008 War Poetry by Winning Writers award.

Candance Reaves is a former English professor, poet and freelance writer "living on an organic farm with her husband and various creatures." Works have appeared in *NMW, Appalachian Life* and elsewhere.

Jonathan Rice's poems have appeared in or are forthcoming from *AGNI Online, Colorado Review, Crab Orchard Review, Gulf Coast, New Delta Review, Sycamore Review, Asheville Poetry Review, Georgetown Review, pacific REVIEW, Witness* and *Best New Poets 2008.* Awards include the 2008 *Gulf Coast* Poetry Prize, 2008 Milton-Kessler Prize from *Harpur Palate,* and the 2008 Yellowwood Prize from *Yalobusha Review.* He received an MFA from Virginia Commonwealth University, where he teaches writing. He is seeking a publisher for his poetry manuscript, CONSTELLARIUM.

SIAM attended Aenon Bible College, Ohio State University, and is a graduate of Harvard Divinity School. He has read and performed in the U.S. and abroad. A co-founder of OSU's *Proud Black Images Magazine*, his works appear widely in many media. He is the author of *A Word for Black Emotion* and *Rain of Grace—New & Selected Poems.* Visit www.*RainofGrace.com.*

Lucy Sieger's essays and articles have been published in *Southern Living, Knoxville News-Sentinel, Metro Pulse, EvaMag* and the anthologies *Low Explosions; A Knoxville Christmas 2007; Outscape: Writings on Fences and Frontiers,* and *Motif: Writing by Ear.* She lives in Knoxville with husband Mark and "two canine babies, Daisy and Jasper."

Barbara Smith-Alfaro has a B.A. in Literature from Goddard College in Vermont and is a graduate of the American Academy of Dramatic Arts in New York. Awards include two Jenny McKean Moore writing scholarships at George Washington University in DC, and a Maryland Arts Council Award in Playwriting. Poems and essays have appeared in *Poet Lore, WordWrights, Minimus, Journal of Kentucky Studies* and *Chesapeake Reader.* She is a member of the Dramatists Guild of America (DG) and Screen Actors Guild (SAG).

Joseph A. Soldati, Portland, OR, is the author of a chapbook, *Apocalypse Clam* (2006); a scholarly book, *Configurations of Faust* (1980); a poetry collection, *Making My Name* (1990) and co-editor of *O Poetry! ¡Oh Poesía! Poems of Oregon and Peru* (1997). *His poems* and essays have appeared in *Poet Lore, Beloved on the Earth, The Litchfield Review, Margie, Line Drives: 100 Contemporary Baseball Poems, Ars Medica: A Journal of Medicine, the Arts and the Humanities* and elsewhere.

Laura Still is a poet and playwright who works as a dental hygienist and sales assistant, a USTA tennis umpire and mother of two. A contributing editor to *NMW*, she's also active in the Knoxville Writers Guild. Her poetry has appeared in anthologies and journals and in her book, *Guardians* (Celtic Cat, 2009). She is the author/director of over 50 children's plays for her church. A selection appears in the teaching manual, *Acts of the Apostles* (2009). She likes to sail, kayak and otherwise travel.

Michael Sweeney, a Pushcart nominee, earned his MFA from Brooklyn College and teaches at Fairfield University. His book, *In Memory of the Fast Break* (Plain View Press) was a finalist for the Nicholas Roerich and Backwaters Prizes. He's been published in *Margie: The American Journal of Poetry, Vol. 6*, and elsewhere.

Ruth Thompson grew up in the San Francisco Bay area and spent her working life in Los Angeles. In 2007, her poem "Fat Time" won a *NMW* Award and she's placed in the William Faulkner/Pirate's Alley poetry contest. Works have appeared in *Sonora Review, Comstock Review, Sow's Ear Poetry Review, River Styx, 13th Moon* and elsewhere. She has a BA from Stanford, Ph.D. in American literature from Indiana University, and has been a professor, librarian, director of community information, college administrator, yoga teacher, and poetry editor of *The Eclipse*. In 2005 she moved to a farmhouse in upstate New York with her long-lost college sweetheart, where she's working on her first book of poems.

Pamela Spiro Wagner is co-author of *Divided Minds: Twin Sisters and their Journey through Schizophrenia* (St Martin's Press, 2005), which won the 2006 national NAMI Outstanding Literature Award and was a finalist for the Connecticut Book Award. Her work has appeared in the *New York Times Sunday Magazine* and *Tikkun.*

Suellen Wedmore, Poet Laureate *emerita* for Rockport, MA, is the author of the chapbook *On Marriage and Other Parallel Universes* (Finishing Line Press). Her chapbook *Deployed* won the Grayson Press Award.

Anthony Russell White "poet, pilgrim and healer" in San Rafael, CA, has been nominated for Pushcarts. Author of eight chapbooks, "four grandsons keep me young."

Alexandra Wild was born in Reutlingen, Germany, and resides in Takoma Park, MD, "or else somewhere on the West Coast." Her poetry has appeared in the *Takoma Voice* and the *Takoma Park Bathroom Poetry Project*. She is working on translations from Ukrainian, German, and Chinese poetry.

Don Williams is a writer, teacher, and founding editor of *New Millennium Writings*.

Ouida Welch Williams, mother, grandmother, great-grandmother, enjoys family, travel, gardening, painting and reading.

Robert Carl Williams, an architect in Pittsfield, VT, grew up in East Tennessee and makes his home in Vermont with his wife, Annabelle. A graduate of UT and Harvard Graduate School of Design, he served in the Air Force as a jet pilot. He and Annabelle spent five months each winter since 1980 sailing westward around the world, concluding in Thailand after 30 years. He has been widely published and is the author of *Low Sweet Notes* (Edwin Mellen Press, 2002).

Diana Woodcock is the author of *Mandala* (Foothills, 2009) part of the *Poets on Peace* series and *Travels of a Gwai Lo* (Toadlily Press, 2009). Honors include an International Publication Award from *Atlanta Review*, the Creekwalker Poetry Prize, an Artists Embassy International Dancing Poetry Festival Prize, residencies at MICA/Rochefort-en-Terre, Vermont Studio Center, Virginia Center for the Creative Arts, and Everglades National Park. Poems have appeared or are forthcoming in *Best New Poets 2008, Nimrod, Atlanta Review, Crab Orchard* Review*, Southern Humanities Review, Portland Review* and others.

Barbara Zimmermann teaches fiction writing at Ball State University. Her fiction, poetry, and literary nonfiction have appeared or are forthcoming in numerous literary journals and anthologies.

~ The NMW Study Guide ~
for Teachers and Writers

*T*his is not about the literary canon. Rather, it's about what's happening now in letters. New Millennium Writings is a sampler of what accomplished amateurs and professionals are sending round to publishers and websites in our astonishing times. These stories, essays and poems represent the best of more than 3,500 works submitted to NMW over a 12-month period spanning 2008 and 2009. Some writers herein have won high honors. Many have books, articles, stories, poems and more in print and online. Others are taking their first bow in these pages and at NewMillenniumWritings.com.

There are lots of ways to approach a collection such as this, and much depends on the level of attainment already achieved.

We recommend that all students and writers read "Break These Rules," beginning on page 208, for a better understanding of our biases, expectations and approaches to the craft, art and intent of writing, whether it be fiction, nonfiction, or poetry. We believe most anyone who reads these "rules" will be better writers almost immediately for the experience. Still, they are guidelines only, as are the discussion questions and exercises below. Think of them as a place to start.

Then, beginning with **Short-short Fiction**, moving through **Fiction, Nonfiction** and ending with our ample **Poetry Suite**, we pose questions regarding selected works for group discussion, personal reflection and writing exercises.

Skip around if you like. You'll find that some of the poetry and short-short fiction make for stimulating *and economical* in-class readings, whether aloud by the leader, round-robin by the group, or in silence. Such short pieces leave ample class time for discussion or writing. At the risk of stating the obvious, longer pieces should be assigned ahead of time for revisiting at future meetings.

On page 203, we offer general ways teachers and writers might utilize this book, and suggest alternative exercises, but first, here is our list of works for group discussion, personal reflection, and writing exercises. We're not suggesting there are definitive answers to questions posed below, in most cases. Each writer or reader must finally determine which answers are right for him or her.

Short-short Fiction

Allison Alsup, *Grass Shrimp*, p. 8: How do the opening two sentences lure the reader in? What is revealed in the last line? Would it change your answer if you learned the author rejects your interpretation (as she did mine)? Which is more valid, authors' intentions or readers' impressions? Why? How does this longstanding literary debate relate to your writing? How do creatively minted words, such as *ghostland,* work for you? What do they add to a piece of writing? Name three striking similes in the story. How does the writer use the five senses? Assess her use of verbs. Are they strong? Do you spot any that might've eliminated the need for adjectives or adverbs? How effective is the phrase, *a brush-like wind paints everything with salt?* What does it suggest about culture, aesthetics and setting?

Examine the Author's Statement: How well does Allison Alsup utilize her concept of "between-ness" in these pages?

Writing Exercise: Compose a few paragraphs or lines of poetry that employ one or two similes that, like the "brush-like wind," serve more than one purpose.

Tim Johnson, *America the Beautiful, p. 12:* How effective is the author's title? Is irony immediately suggested? Is a sentence like, *God I hate that song,* effective? Should it be taken as the author's last word on the subject? Describe the narrator of this story in a few words. How is he or others changed by the end of the story? Who is the protagonist? Is it the narrator? The primary singer? The community as a whole? America herself? In what ways is dialogue herein comparable to ping-pong? How well does the author handle what we call *choreography,* the physical placement and movements of characters within the story's physical setting? Did you have an emotional reaction to this story?

Examine the Author's Statement: Boil it down to one telling phrase. Do you agree? How well does the author follow his own advice?

Writing Exercise: Picture a confrontation involving two or more characters. Practice choreography, moving them around in time and space as your story progresses. Start writing. Examine other writers' choreography. Is it effective?

Barbara Zimmermann, *Southern Discomfort, p. 18:* How effective is the thumbnail sketch of the protagonist's appearance here? The impressionistic description of setting? How does the author reveal social status and background? What is the effect of inserting the brand name *Tabu* into the narrative?

Examine the Author's Statement: What character from literature or drama do you believe the protagonist is based on? If you read the Author's Statement before reading the story, do you believe it helped or hindered your appreciation?

Writing Exercise: Choose a famous character or historical figure and place him or her in a modern setting. Start writing.

Longer Fiction

Steve Fayer, *Calliope, p. 24:* Note the multiplicity of narrative forms—storytelling, dreams, memories, flashbacks, dialogue and so forth. How does Steve Fayer braid these narratives into one story? How does each setting in time and space resonate with the others? Even though Ditch and Calliope love one another, their dialogue exhibits tension, even conflict. How is this achieved? How does it serve to hold the reader's interest? How does the author reveal social status and background? How does this approach differ from that in "Southern Discomfort" or other works? Fayer echoes several racial and ethnic epithets and stereotypes. Are these offensive in this context? Why or why not? What is the effect of inserting the brand name *M&Ms* into this story? We've all heard, *show, don't tell,* but Fayer does a good bit of both. Does this approach work? Is the ending of this story convincing? Affecting? Prepared for? What is the overall theme?

Examine the Author's Statement: Have you ever been inspired to write by a found object such as a photograph, letter or journal? Is there any object around your apartment, dorm or house that would serve as material for fiction, poetry, article or essay? On whom do you base characters or poetry personas?

Writing Exercise: Look around the place you live, or the setting you're in now and select an object on which to base a story, article or poem. Start writing.

Rusty Dolleman, *Sheepdog, 43:* Analyze the story's central metaphor, as suggested by the title. Does it work? How effective is the opening line? Does it reveal the narrator to be altogether reliable? Look at dialogue here. Does it move quickly back and forth? Is it tension-filled, even among characters who like each other? How does the author let the reader know who's talking, even when he doesn't explicitly state the identity? How does the author choreograph the physical location and movement of his characters within the story? Point to a scene in which this is important to revealing character and relationships? Like many of the writers herein, Dolleman writes from the POV of someone very different from himself. Is he effective? How does the author quickly suggest to readers that his narrator is female? Dolleman omits quotation marks in flashback passages. Does this make dialogue harder to read? Do you know of other authors who do this?

Examine the Author's Statement: What does Dolleman mean by, "The only question writers should ask themselves is *Did I work today?*" How does this square with your own approach?

Writing Exercise: Write a story or vignette from the perspective of a person of a different gender, race, age, ethnicity, class or community from your own.

Nonfiction

Katharine Goodridge Ingram, *Swimming Under Salvador, p. 58:* Can you count the number of senses employed in this story? What about a sixth sense? When the young protagonist vividly "sees" the destruction inside Salvador's studio, does this hint at extrasensory perception? Heightened awareness? Over-vivid imagination? Is such surrealism a dangerous ploy? Does it work here? Discuss *personification* in the story, especially regarding landscape and water. Cite similes herein that employ this technique. In this work of creative nonfiction do any particular passages read as if contrived or fictive? Is this problematical? What techniques do you find here that you also find in the fiction or poetry herein? Any differences? What are they?

Examine the Author's Statement: Do you belong to a critique group or other workshop? Have you found it to be helpful to your writing? Your well-being?

Writing Exercises: Write something in which you employ personification. Now write something in which you employ a sixth sense, such as ESP, apparitions, unlikely coincidences or heightened awareness.

Melanie M. Hoffert, *The Allure of Grain Trucks, p. 68:* I would argue that landscape is a character in this essay. How does the author achieve this effect? How does the theme of silence serve to unite two other themes of the essay— sexual identity and geographic identity. How are both revealed as determinative of destiny? How do both relate to the notion of a dying way of life? Of the works discussed so far, this essay is the only one to chronicle true experiences in the narrator's *recent* past. Is this an asset? Does this make the story easier to believe and identify with? Why or why not? Note the use of 'I'? How many paragraphs and/or sentences begin with this pronoun? Compare this to other first-person stories, essays and poems herein. Which are most successful? Why?

Examine the Author's Statement: Do you agree that "the most damaging silences are... those we carry within?" If so, how does this affect your own choice of subject matter and approaches as a writer? Is it possible to be too frank in your writing, even in the first draft? If you suppress shameful or embarrassing events or qualities in your first draft, do you risk shutting doors on memories a more honest approach might open to view?

Writing Exercise: F. Scott Fitzgerald once said that memories we're ashamed to talk about often make for good stories. Write about an experience in your life that embarrasses you to talk about. Note in a journal what you learn from this experience. Does it open doors to other memories? Are they richer than materials you're not embarrassed to talk about?

Lucy Sieger, *Domestic Insurgency, p. 84:* Like the first taste of a homemade cake, these opening lines seduce. Otherwise, is the simile evoked to introduce the cake a useful one? Does it succeed in establishing the tone of this? It's theme? Does it evoke tension? Personality? Does the essay live up to this beginning? Although this is about a failed marriage, it's far from tragic. What are the author's attitudes toward the marriage discussed herein? Point to aspects of language that carry on her initial playful tone? What is the saddest line in the essay? Why?

Examine the Author's Statement: Does Lucy Sieger realize her intent "to spin a unique perspective, one that relates a particular episode to universal emotions?" If so, name some universals evoked by this "particular episode."

Writing Exercise: Come up with an audacious metaphor to use in an opening line. Now write.

Don Williams, *John Updike at Rest, p. 88:*
Of all the writers represented in this book, the late John Updike is/was the most successful, based on public honors, book sales and media coverage. Take a few minutes to underline all the writing advice he offers here regarding technique, habits and philosophies. Updike says, for instance, "When you come to the practice of your art you have to go with what thrills you. If you wrote some opposite way, you would get criticized for that. You have to please yourself." Do you agree? How would that advice go over in your workshop? And he asks, "What is the point of most of the fiction you read? It seems to have no point... Tolstoy and Dickens have a wonderful sense of something big grinding away. It's hard to produce that now. A lot of the big writers—for instance Fredric Barthelme comes to mind and Bobbie Ann Mason—seem to be saying life is just a series of blips on the TV screen...." How effectively are Updike's approach to science, sex, God and writing revealed? Discuss.

Discuss brief examples of Updike's poetry in the article. Now read a legendary short story by Updike, such as "A&P" (not included but available online), then take another look at the discussion questions in the preceding paragraph.

Writing exercise: Interview someone about their beliefs regarding primal issues, such as sex, God and art. Write something based on this interview. *(Email DonWilliams7@charter.net for a free tip-sheet on The Art of the Interview.)*

*

Continued...

Poetry

Naomi Ruth Lowinsky, *Madelyn Dunham, Passing On, p. 104:* How effective is the opening line? Did it pull you in? What is the effect of the repeated 's' sounds in lines 2, 3 & 4? Who is the speaker of the poem? Describe her voice. What is a slack-key guitar? How is it used in this poem? How crucial is the information in the footnote to understanding the poem? How important is the juxtaposition of celebration to mournfulness? What does the poet mean by, *the land where they know how to feed the dead?* Long vowel sounds can lend a haunted quality or mournful tone to writing. How many long vowel sounds do you count here? Is this poem too political for literary anthologies?

Examine the Author's Statement: Do you agree that "There is a place in poetry where the spiritual and the political meet?" Does reading the poet's entire statement affect your response?

Writing Exercise: Write a short essay about why you agree or disagree with the central theme in this poem. What emotion(s) does this poem evoke? Why?

Ed Frankel, *An Altar For Uncle Joe, p. 115:* What items does the speaker of the poem gather to place on his altar? How does such a catalogue bring Uncle Joe alive for the reader? In line 8 of the third stanza, the phrase, *twice rate of a human heart* appears. What's the effect of omitting *the* from that line? Is there a tradeoff, and if so, what is it? What is the effect of the repeated 't's and 'd's in the next line? What's gained by *the* in the following? *whatever else it was that took you out of the life?* Compare *the* to the omitted *the* discussed previously. Again, is there a tradeoff? If so, what does this say about writing and art? Is it necessary to appreciate jazz to appreciate this poem? How does this poem resemble jazz? Does a free-form jazz sensibility inform its structure?

Examine the Author's Statement: Does the information about inspirations and sources here increase your appreciation of the poem? Why or why not?

Writing Exercise: Make an altar to someone you love, living or dead. Catalogue the things you'd place on such an altar.

Trish Lindsey Jaggers, *On the Night They Took Your Life, p. 119:* Briefly summarize the story within the poem. How many senses does the author employ? What about the so-called sixth sense? Analyze line breaks in this poem. How effective are they? Note all the primal, celestial, and earthy words that arrive at the end of lines—*moon, stars, baby, breast, life, mouth, ring, feet, earth, sky, name, you, me, warm, edge*—words that linger for an extra heartbeat because of placement. Is there a lesson here for prose writers? What is the effect of the repeated words in the last line? Build an imaginary altar for the deceased in the poem. Now draw items from the poem to place on it.

Examine the Author's Statement: Summarize the story within this statement. What philosophy of poetry and aesthetics is contained in the last lines? How does it compare to the story in the poem?

Suggested Exercise: Restate the essence of the Author's Statement as a short poem.

Ruth Thompson, *Speaking of the Muse, p. 124:* Who is the speaker's muse? Describe her voice. What is the effect of beginning the first line of the third grouping with 'O'? Is there a pattern or unifying theme to the poem's imagery?

Name, describe or otherwise define the pattern. Do you have a "muse" in the form of a concept, philosophy or other wellspring that inspires you as a writer?

Writing Exercise: Compose a poem to or from your "muse," real or imagined.

Aliene Pylant, *Gardens, 2001, p. 126:* What is the rhyme pattern of this poetry? Is it effective? Do the rhymes fall from your lips naturally or are they forced? The artist uses *garden* both as subject and metaphor. Does this work? Is she consistent? Why or why not?

Writing Exercise: Compose a rhymed poem of more than 20 lines.

Madelyn Camrud, *The Pulse, p. 133:* This poem brought tears to the eyes of an aging couple associated with *NMW*. Can you see why? What images and techniques of language lend this poem its mournfulness. Compare its use of the word *song* to the same word in Ellen Bihler's poem, *Red Barns*, p. 131. Read *The Pulse* with or to someone close. Does it change the reading experience for you?

Writing Exercise: Compose a poem about the imagined loss of an intimate friend or lover.

Eric Lester, *Blushed, p. 139:* What ancient poetic form does the author employ in this short poem? What is the rhyme scheme? Theme? Meter. Discuss the use of personification. It's been said that some of Shakespeare's sonnets are better if the last rhymed couplet were omitted. How effective is Lester's couplet?

Writing Exercise: Compose a poem utilizing personification. Now, retaining the personification, re-write it as a sonnet.

Stephanie Elliott, *What the Tattoo Artist Said, p. 147:* What is the major theme of this poem? What sort of world does it describe? How does the opening line undermine or reinforce the notion of such a world? Is the last line effective? Why or why not? Note the use of alliteration. Is it effective?

Writing Exercise: Write a poem, short-short story or vignette about a tattoo adorning yourself or someone you know.

Leland James, *Dreamscape, p. 149:* I liked this poem a lot, perhaps you do as well, but try putting into words what it's all about.

Writing Exercise: Compose a poem or a few paragraphs that are impenetrable in literal terms, yet evocative on a spiritual, intellectual or metaphysical level.

Peter Lopatin, *You Are Here, p. 153:* What is the central theme? Is there a message herein? What means are used to enhance transitions and weave the poem together? Is there a pattern or unifying theme to the similes? How is the notion of journeys, employed?

Writing Exercise: Write a work in the form of your choosing that involves an ongoing image, motif or pattern of similes.

Pat Landreth Keller, *Not for Publication, p. 156:* Do you like the title? Re-read the last five lines. What do they mean? What does this poem suggest about those who choose the poet's life? Is this a cautionary poem? Who is Roethke?

Writing Exercise: In the form of your choosing express your fears about taking up the writer's life and your chances for success, as society defines it.

Cathy Kodra, *Bell Curve, p. 159:* Can you name the formal structure of this poem? Write down the rhyme scheme. What is the poem's theme?

Writing Exercise: Pick a topic of your choosing and write a poem using this structure, form and rhyme scheme.

Ellen LaFlèche, *What My French-Canadian Grandmother Said In Response To The Fears About The Anthrax Postal Attacks of 2001, p. 161:* Is this poem believable? Is it enchanting in any way? If so, how? Does this lesson from 1910 bring perspective to life a century later? Is there a lesson here for writers and reporters?

Writing Exercise: Compose a poem based on wisdom, advice, folly, or a colorful story related by a late relative or friend about a long dead relation of theirs.

David Krump, *The Bull Moose Sum, p. 162:* Is there humor in lines 6&7? Note the consonance of the lines, *A constant / hiss as snow settled...* What associations does the poem's last word evoke? What is the central image of the poem?

Writing Exercise: Look around you. What is the dominant organic or geologic object you see? Now imagine the past and nature of such a thing or creature. Write.

Sarah Matè, *Night Train to Memphis, p. 165:* Name three things you like about this poem. How does the author bring each of the two strangers discussed alive for the reader? What do the last three lines mean?

Writing Exercise: Turn down the lights, close your eyes. As you take several deep breaths, stretch and then relax all major muscle groups in your body in turn. Inhale, exhale deeply as you imagine you're on a train rolling through the countryside. You watch the dimming of the day out your window until lights on the horizon blend with stars in the sky. Looking up you see a dusky, yet familiar, figure walking toward you down the aisle. This person stops, hands you a box, then turns without a word and leaves. Now turn up the lights and write a poem or paragraphs that engage the following questions: Who is the familiar figure? What's in the box she or he handed to you? What is its significance? Is the familiar figure someone you know personally? Someone famous? Imaginary? Is she/he living or dead?

Pamela Spiro Wagner, *Three, For Those Left Behind, p. 180:* *The lake shimmers, ebony splashed with silver...* How evocative is that phrase? Now look at it in context. Why do you suppose the poet broke these lines just so? Is there yet even more pleasing language here? In the second stanza, Pamela Spiro Wagner could be charged with mixing metaphors. Does this detract from the beauty of her language?

Writing Exercise: Give yourself 15 minutes to compose a short poem or several paragraphs employing the most gorgeous language you can summon. Tough going? If so, lower your standards and start again with the goal of just getting something, anything down on paper. Let it cool, then come back another day and embellish with care. Assess which approach worked best for you?

Lansing King, *Piper, p. 188:* Does this poem evoke an earlier time? Does it evoke the lift and sweep of flight? If so, how is this achieved? Even though this poem is written in second person, is the use of *you* always plural? Singular? Is the *you* referred to in the next to last stanza the same as *you* referenced in the opening lines? If not, describe each version of *you*. Is this shift effective? Describe the final simile of the poem. Compare it to the "brush-like wind" of the first story we discussed, "Shrimp Grass," by Allison Alsup, p. 8.

Writing Exercise: Write a poem or paragraph in second person, employing *you* as a singular personal pronoun. Now write a poem or paragraph suggesting that *you* really means *I*.

*

Other Suggested Exercises:

1. Read widely herein with an eye to discerning what sorts of stories, poems, essays and articles were getting published in 2009-10. Scan biographical notes, pp. 190-95, for a sense of honors and publication histories represented here, and the cross-section of American letters herein.

2. Take an hour to examine and discuss all authors' statements, noting the wide range of approaches to craft, writing habits, sources, subjects and philosophies.

3. Take time to read aloud and discuss, "Break These Rules," starting on p. 208 and continuing on p. 204, then lead a discussion. Where do you agree or disagree? Ask for examples, exceptions, objections, and/or support for specific rules. Discuss "the nexus of fiction, nonfiction and poetry." What rules *don't* apply to all?

4. Briefly discuss the *Quick Tour* introduction and Obama section. Is there a place for politics in literary discussions? Were the editors misguided in allowing political opinions herein? Is Obama's "Pop" a worthy poem? What are its weaknesses?

5. Assign the writing exercise below or others of your choosing. Vary lengths of assignments from a few paragraphs or lines up to several pages....

* Write a short-short story or vignette, 1000 words or less, based on someone you consider different from you. Bring that person's world alive for readers.

* Interview or converse with someone from another religion, culture, race, ethnicity, gender, age group, or class, then try the first exercise again.

* Write a one-page story or poem based on people you know in your hometown.

* Take a week to try the following: On Day One go for a short run. Day Two whirl around for five minutes or two. Day Three drink something stronger than tea. Day Four, meditate, then meditate some more. Day Five get up before daylight. Day Six alter your consciousness with some other trick. Each day, after you're done, start writing a story, essay or poem. Day Seven, compare the results.

* Lower the lights, then lead some friends or fellow writers through a short, guided meditation in which they close their eyes, take deep breaths, relax, then pair off by turning to their nearest neighbor. Have them clasp hands for two full minutes. Raise the lights and ask each to write a paragraph describing their fellows' hands.

* Write something that artfully employs a phrase from another language.

* Convene outside, ask your fellow writers to close their eyes for five minutes and write down what they hear. Five minutes after they start writing, compare notes. How well did members' perceptions coincide?

* Look at the snapshots and artful sketches in this book. Choose one that you find affecting and write about it as if unrelated to the work with which it appears.

* Think of some concept or place of which you know little and write down the surest thing you know about the subject.

* Keep a journal for one week, describing your activities, cataloguing the things around you, describing the places you are, chronicling any conflicts observed or experienced. Let it cool for another week, then re-read. Now write a poem, story, essay or article based on one or more journal entries. Wait one month, then try again.

* Write a short story, article or poem in present tense. Now re-write in past tense. Which seems more immediate? Which carries more gravitas? Is there a tradeoff?

* Write down the truest thing you know about what's most on your mind.

* Write down the truest thing you know about your life. How does this relate to themes found in your writing?

* Re-writing is often the most fulfilling phase, so let your first rush of language cool, then make it better. Reading aloud is helpful in identifying phrases that cause you to stumble. These need revising.
* When it comes to structure, make chronology your default position, unless time-hopping is a central theme. It's ok to start *in media res* and flash back, but be wary of too many flashbacks, especially flashbacks *within* flashbacks. One who famously breaks this rule is Kurt Vonnegut, Jr. In novel after novel he goes time-hopping. For most, however, a good place to start—or flash back to early on—is the chronological beginning.
* Begin with a strong opening line. Often this starts with the third or fifth paragraph of your first draft. Sometimes it's the last line of what you thought was the final version. Rarely is it the first thing you set down.
* Pulitzer Prize-winning novelist Richard Ford (*Independence Day*) once compared opening lines to handshakes. A good strong handshake conveys the impression that this new relationship will be of consequence.
* A strong opening line does one or more of the following: honestly hooks the reader, alludes to a theme, describes a character, sets a tone, places a story in motion, poses a mystery, sets a rhythm. It should contain the DNA from which your story, poem or article will grow.
* Hook your reader by creating conflict or tension by the end of the first sentence, first paragraph, first page, first chapter and so on. Make your protagonist angry, thirsty, in jeopardy, sad, curious, lost or in some other strait that makes the agent, editor or general reader keep reading.
* Pull your reader along by providing strong transitions, especially between paragraphs. Pick up a rhythm, a figure of speech, a crisp, memorable image, a word, vowel or consonant from the previous paragraph, and link to it in such a way that your work is interwoven, braided, hard to break.
* To make your writing a page-turner, try shorter sentences, shorter paragraphs, or else go the opposite route, rendering them serpentine, incantatory, irresistible, by imposing hypnotic rhythms like William Faulkner or Cormac McCarthy, just not all the time. *Variety* rules.
* Vary your sentence lengths.
* Write efficiently. Every line should advance your story. Make description earn its keep by embellishing setting, character, theme or plot.
* Let verbs carry the action. Read Hemingway, Willa Cather, Raymond Carver and other masters of verbs. Go back and look at yours. Consult a thesaurus. A strong verb will eliminate adverbs and adjectives. Use "sauntered," for example, rather than "walked leisurely" or "festooned in ribbons" rather than, say, "draped in sweeping loops of ribbon." Strong verbs bring life to prose and poetry and speed the plough.
* Avoid static or general verbs such as *did, came, had, was, got, moved.* Find verbs that express nuance and shades, such as *built, ran, possessed, bought, borrowed, stole, skipped, drove, pushed.*

* Avoid bureaucratic words. *Mostly* is better than *primarily* in most cases.
* Liposuction your writing, in the words of novelist and agent Sol Stein.
* Cut *qualifiers*—words and phrases that reduce the power of language, such as... *it seems, could be, sort of, might have, a little, a tiny bit, what you might call, I think, in some ways, you could say, more or less.*
* Choose the stronger of two paired adjectives and adverbs, eliminating one. The use of lots of paired adjectives is the mark of a beginner.
* Use specific adjectives. *Cranberry*, not red. *Haggard*, not tired. *Diabetic*, not sick. *Serpentine*, not long.
* Minimize interruptions for background (also known as exposition). While it's nearly impossible to avoid past-perfect constructions in prose, *had been* for instance, try to limit dependence on such helping words.
* Avoid repeating the same word too often, especially "I," and especially at the beginning of sentences and paragraphs, even in first-person works. To achieve this, make the thing observed the subject of your next sentence. Try, "A tree crashed against the back window, blocking my path," rather than "I tried entering by the back window, but a tree crashed into it, blocking my path..." especially if lots of other sentences begin with I.
* Avoid filler words, like *very* and *quite*. "I love you" is just as powerful as "I love you very much," and more eloquent. "He's strong" is stronger than "he's quite strong" unless you're making a class distinction through dialogue.
* Other words easy to prune are *that* and *the*. Read this sentence, then decide whether to keep each *the* in parentheses. "(The) rooms below were shadow-haunted in (the) evening light, save for the yellow glow from the kitchen door." Losing *the* lends mystery to a phrase at times, by turning things into concepts. Apply this notion with care, however.
* Use rhythm and alliteration to good advantage. Phrases like "constant chorus" or "serious whispers," with their repeated sounds, mean what they say and say what they mean. "He <u>strode</u> a-<u>cross</u> the <u>room</u> to <u>her</u>," with its alternate stressed syllables, provides the rhythm of walking. Read lots of good poetry and prose stylists. Repeat long vowel sounds in moody or mournful pieces.
* Use the active voice rather than the passive. <u>Active</u>: "The lawyer snatched the guard's Glock and shot the judge." <u>Passive</u>: "The judge was shot by the lawyer, who snatched the Glock belonging to the guard." The passive voice has been called the voice of Watergate: "Mistakes were made, yes, a break-in did occur." It's a voice that postpones responsibility and stalls for time. Not hallmarks of fluid narrative.
* Make simple past tense your default position, but don't be afraid to go with present tense if it's better suited to your material. Present tense offers immediacy, briskness, but it tends to undermine *gravitas* or seriousness. Play with such trade-offs. Learn to employ them with finesse.

* Avoid clichés, because we use too many of them to shake a stick at without even knowing it.

* Surprise your reader. Plant mystery—reasons for wonder—in your garden of words. Use moments of transcendence, the supernatural and coincidence, but subtly prepare the reader for the latter, so she/he doesn't feel cheated.

* Astonish the reader with opposites. Opposite moods, characters, emotions, actions or physical attributes. A little man with huge appetites. "The best of times, the worst of times."

* Show, don't tell. Don't say, "Annabelle was a kindly woman who was good to animals." Rather, try, "Annabelle held a crust toward the skittish collie and cooed, 'Easy now, come to Mama.'"

* Make your characters distinctive. Give them limps, warts, scars, obsessions, fears, dreams, mannerisms, scents, styles, even politics and religion, although these must be handled carefully, lest ye preach, brethren. I'm often reminded of how Dustin Hoffman builds his film personas, by giving all of them distinctive ways of talking and walking. Think of the distinctive ways he walks in *Tootsie, Midnight Cowboy, Rain Man, Marathon Man* and others....

* Create a world by bringing all *six* senses into play. Reveal how a place feels, sounds, looks, tastes, smells and *seems*. "Joe paused on the stairs and savored the aroma of cornbread baking in his mother's oven, then ran his hand along the worn banister as he tiptoed down the steps. The rooms below were shadow-haunted in evening light, save for the yellow glow from the kitchen door. He heard his mother's deep alto humming 'Rock of Ages Cleft for Me.'"

* Lend mystique by bringing the sixth sense into play. Sparingly (or not) allow your characters intuition, visions, ghosts, feelings, omens, dreams and coincidences. Shakespeare did, Tennyson did. James Agee did. Gabriel García Márquez did. Isabel Allende and others do so today.

* Create a world by cataloging the gear, clothing, possessions and other items surrounding your characters. "Joe stepped in the doorway. Bright fishing flies spangled his hat. He held a roll-your-own cigarette behind each ear, and his sportsman's vest bulged with sandwiches and candy bars. An antique filet knife decorated his right hip." Two writers who catalogued relentlessly were Walt Whitman and John Updike. We know how Brooklyn Ferry sounded, looked and smelt before the Civil War thanks to Whitman's poem, "Crossing Brooklyn Ferry." John Updike brilliantly captured the sights, sounds, fashions and sexual sensibilities of four decades in his series of novels about a character nicknamed Rabbit. Each book covered a decade in the mid to late 20th century. Such catalogues can be tiresome, however, unless delivered with a lyrical quality or engaging technique. Practice this.

* Dialogue should move like ping-pong, briskly, tension-filled even among friends, with only occasional breaks for attribution or description. Make it sound natural and not freighted with background information or too much exposition, especially educational freight. No one wants to hear a character begin talking like an encyclopedia. Use a minimum of attribution, especially if it's obvious from context who's speaking.

* Use "dialect" and slang sparingly, as they can be hard to translate, off-putting, even offensive, as such techniques can suggest class snobbery.

* Don't mix your metaphors and similes. Don't say, "Ali was in the driver's seat (a car simile), his arms spinning like windmills (windmill simile) and the fat lady was tuning up (opera)." Be consistent.

* Use fresh similes, and ones that advance your theme. Linking figures of speech, as Ken Kesey does in *One Flew Over the Cuckoo's Nest*, can result in profound reading experiences. Read this book, noting the many Christ similes subtly associated with protagonist, Randle P. McMurphy, and early-industrial similes about Chief Broom, the semi-reliable narrator.

* Validate reasonable questions or objections readers might raise by acknowledging them, even when you don't agree. "But that's what really happened" is not a good reason for failing to acknowledge it when your writing sounds far-fetched. A phrase such as, "I know it sounds strange," or, "I could hardly believe it," is often all it takes to defuse incredulity.

* Ask yourself three things about everything you write:

1. "Whose story is it?" Who, in the story, essay or poem, is changed by events? This might be the narrator, it could be the "main character" or even the community. Usually, in a good work you'll be able to tell.

2. "Why should the reader care?" Have I built a level of suspense or tension that will make the reader keep reading all the way to the end of my poem, story, article or book? Have I invoked universal themes such as life, death, initiation, marriage, redemption, cruelty, survival, mid-life crisis, romance, awe, wonder, absurdity, blessedness, despair, loneliness, envy, betrayal, shame, vanity, pride, regret, hope, ambition, class-consciousness? Few works encompass *all* such notions, but most encompass one or many.

3. "Have I created a world?" Have I brought all five senses—plus the sixth—into play? Have I shown how my setting smells, tastes, feels, sounds, looks and *seems*? Have I given impressions and/or catalogued the stuff in this new world of mine? Answering these questions can tell you whether you're moving in the right direction.

* Finally, get in a zone. Try to set aside distractions of the day unless employing them in your work. Remember, writing is a synthesis of all you are. Leave analysis for later. Dive deeply into things that matter most, acknowledging *tone*—the mood or quality of your narrator's heart—from the beginning. Look inside to discover how you really feel about your material, then let it flow.

~ End ~

Don Williams
Break These Rules...

*M*ost every writer has, *for expediency, for style, to solve otherwise intractable problems, or just to be ornery. Whatever your reason, you should consider what's lost.*

Like most art, writing is about trade-offs. A *New Yorker* cartoon once depicted a workshop participant, finger to brow, asking archly: "So which was it, Mr. Dickens, the best of times or the worst of times?" as the stricken author looked on. There's a downside to virtually every choice. Maybe that's why Randall Jarrell once defined the novel as "a prose narrative of some length that has something wrong with it."

Still, such guidelines as the following are not arbitrary. They're here because they've worked for someone, sometime, some place. The following notions have all worked for me and writers I know, one way or another. So at least consider them as a place to start. See which are consistent with your own vision, subject matter, voice, style or tone.

* Tone is destiny, in the same way a movie's soundtrack suggests things to come. Sinuous saxophones are for intrigues and passions of *film noir*. Singing violins suggest purer romance. Kazoos are for comedy. So establish tone—the quality of your narrator's soul—in the first paragraph, first *line* if possible. I learned early on that my articles, stories and columns come easy once I set my tone. Let first words instill mystery, excitement, humor, sorrow, intrigue, suspicion, practicality, wit, folksiness or, say, an epic quality. Make all else answer that bell.

* When suffering writer's block, "lower your standards," in the words of Jay McInerney (*Bright Lights, Big City*). Get words down, then revise, revise... more on that later.

* Or do as Hemingway did, write down the truest thing you know, but remember, literal truth is not the only sort of truth, especially in fiction & poetry. To paraphrase Ken Kesey (*One Flew Over the Cuckoo's Nest*), *Some things are true even if they didn't happen.*

* Never fudge the truth on your first private draft, especially if writing memoir, as most every true memory opens doors to deeper memories or visions. Only you know how much truth you can handle, however.

Continued on p. 204...